SELECTED LIST OF CHORUSES

FOR WOMEN'S VOICES

SELECTED LIST OF CHORUSES
FOR WOMEN'S VOICES

THIRD EDITION

Revised and enlarged

Compiled by

ARTHUR WARE LOCKE

Professor Emeritus of Music

Smith College

and

CHARLES K. FASSETT

Instructor of Music and Choral Director

Wheaton College

Published by

SMITH COLLEGE

Northampton, Massachusetts

1964

Preface

The Third Edition of *Selected List of Choruses for Women's Voices* represents a complete revision as well as an attempt to bring the *Selected List* up to date. Many compositions which appeared in the Second Edition have been omitted because they were out-of-print or, in view of the improved publishing standards, seemed unworthy of inclusion. The additions are, for the most part, music that has been published since 1946, the date of the Second Edition. We make no claim for inclusiveness, though we have examined with care a great amount of music that we have obtained from most of the chief publishers of choral music in this country and England as well as from a number of European firms.

In this Third Edition one alphabetical listing for all composers has been adopted instead of grouping composers in different chronological periods as in the Second Edition. Whatever disadvantage this may have is offset by the chronological listing of composers in Section III, Indices.

In general, the *Selected List* is now—partly for lack of space —restricted to works originally composed for treble or equal voices. This does not imply that the editors do not recognize the musical value of many arrangements of works originally composed for other media as well as the many excellent arrangements of folk songs. For instance, *The Concord Song Book for Women's Voices,* published by E. C. Schirmer, is not included in this 3d edition although it is highly recommended by the editors. Of the 98 selections in this admirable collection, an overwhelming majority are arrangements and folk songs.

Although it has been the intention of the editors to exclude arrangements, the question of whether a piece is an arrangement or not has, at times, been difficult to determine. The editors realize the unreliability of their determinations in such publications as *The John Playford Collection of Vocal Part Music* (OxJP) where the editor, W. G. Whittaker, states that "some" alterations have, in certain compositions, been made to adapt the music for women's voices; also in the compositions of John Hilton published by Stainer and Bell (indicated as SB Ayres). A few arrangements have been included quite arbitrarily by the editors on the ground of their musical value, such as *Simple Gifts,* arranged by Irving Fine from Copland's *Appalachian Spring*, and *Praise ye the name of the Lord* by Kastalsky arranged by Gorokhoff. In a sense, too, all the numerous settings of chorales included in the *List* are arrangements. However, a distinction has been made between the settings of chorales in a collection such as *Das Wochenlied,* which has been included, and the rearrangement of settings by Bach and other composers, as in the two books of chorales for women's voices, arranged by E. Harold Geer and published by E. C. Schirmer, which have not been included. The settings in *Das Wochenlied,* unlike Mr. Geer's fine arrangements, are original compositions on a given melody.

In Catholic liturgical music there are many compositions for women's voices that fall into the category of music intended primarily for inclusion in the Roman Catholic service. Many of these works are of fine musical quality yet have not been included because of their specialized nature. Settings of *Tantum ergo* and *O Salutaris hostia* as well as other less known texts can be found in the catalogs of such firms as World Library of Sacred Music (WLSM), J. Fischer (JF), and McLaughlin and Reilly (MR).

The entry for each piece is in two parts, separated by a semi-colon; the information before the semicolon pertains to the composition, after the semicolon to a particular edition of that piece. Semicolons separate subsequent edition citations where there are more than one for a given composition.

Entries are arranged alphabetically by title or first line, in the original language, where it is known. The title is differentiated from the first line by means of a dash where the two are different. Translations of either are given in parentheses. Following the title and first line further identifying information is often given; this may be an opus number or a thematic-catalog number. References may also be to Complete Works (MoTO, ScW, etc.) or Collected Editions (DTÖ, MB, etc.). These citations permit the conductor to study a suggested composition in these sources in order to determine its suitability before actually purchasing a performing edition.

After the identifying information, the source of the text has been given where such a determination has been practicable. The symbol T: is used to show text sources. In Biblical references Roman numerals indicate chapters or Psalms, Arabic numerals, verses. All Biblical citations are to the King James version; other translations of the Bible may vary in numbering.

Voicing, accompaniment, duration and grade of difficulty appear immediately before the semicolon; alternate voices or accompaniment are in parentheses. Duration is in minutes and seconds, i.e., 1:30 means one minute and thirty seconds. When duration designation is used in conjunction with x2, or x3, etc., this indicates the number of times the same music is repeated either with the same text or a different verse. In settings of the Mass each section is timed separately and indicated with an identifying abbreviation (Ky 2:10, Gl 2:15, etc.). In this way one may also determine how much of the Mass is set to music. Duration indications should be considered as only approximate. It was not practicable for the editors to time each piece exactly; also, ideas of tempi vary. Realizing that the duration designation could not be absolutely correct, the editors believed nonetheless that it would be a valuable aid to the users of the *Selected List.*

The designation of grade of difficulty has been hard to judge; what is easy for one conductor and singing group may be difficult for another. In general, this determination has been made for each piece in relation to the period in which it was written. Obviously, a piece of medium difficulty in the Romantic idiom may seem easy when compared to a 20th-century composition.

The second part of an entry, relating to an edition, follows the semicolon. Any deviation from the information about the composition, such as "Eng text only" or "accompaniment missing," is given at this point. Unless otherwise indicated, it may be assumed that the edition conforms to the description given in the first part of the entry. When more than one edition is cited, each is separated by a semicolon.

Citations to editions may refer either to a single publication or to a piece within a collection. The designation *in,* immediately prior to the actual edition citation, invariably indicates a publication of more than one composition.

Publications containing two or three pieces. As part of the edition identification the companion piece or pieces are given using the symbol w/ (with). If a companion piece is by the same composer as that of the title entry, his name is not repeated; compositions by different composers are so indicated.

Publications containing four or more pieces. Collections of music by a single composer are given, with the contents, in Section I. Collections containing works by more than one composer are given in Section II, *Collections.*

Acknowledgments

The editors have made use of Erich Valentin's *Handbuch der Chormusik,* Volume I, 1953, and Volume II, 1958 (Regensburg: Gustav Bosse Verlag). Though the *Handbuch* covers the whole field of choral music, there are extensive separate sections devoted to music for treble voices.

Recent bibliographical information is given in the article under "Frauenchor" in Volume IV of *Die Musik in Geschichte und Gegenwart* (Kassel: Bärenreiter-Verlag, 1955).

Annette Friedrich's *Beiträge zur Geschichte des weltlichen Frauenchor im 19. Jahrhundert in Deutschland* (Regensburg: Gustav Bosse Verlag, 1961) contains a list of music for women's choruses and also a bibliography relating to the general subject.

Merrill Knapp's excellent *Selected List of Music for Men's Voices* (Princeton, New Jersey: Princeton University Press, 1952) has affected the handling of certain features of the catalog such as the references to collections.

The production of this volume has been made possible by the generous understanding of the administrative officers of Smith College and the Department of Music for which we are profoundly grateful.

To Mrs. Mary Ankudowich, Music Librarian of Smith College, go our heartfelt thanks for her constant and unfailing help.

ARTHUR W. LOCKE AND CHARLES K. FASSETT, *Editors*

Contents

Abbreviations and Publishers

A	alto
acc	accompanied, accompaniment
ad lib.	ad libitum
Affiliated	Affiliated Musicians, Los Angeles. Now incorporated into Mills Music, 1619 Broadway, New York, N.Y.
Ag	Agnus Dei
AJ	Arthur Jordan Choral Series, Marks Music Corp.
AM	Associated Music Publishers, Inc., 25 W. 45th St., New York 19, N.Y.
anon	anonymous
arr	arrangement, arranged by
Arrow	Arrow Music Press, New York. Obtain through BoHa.
ATD	Archibald T. Davison
Au	Augener, Ltd., London. Obtain through Galaxy.
B	Bass
Bä	Bärenreiter-Verlag, 35 Heinrich Schütz Allee, Kassel, West Germany.
Bank	Bank, Annie, Amsterdam. Obtain through WLSM.
BB	Bote und Bock, Germany. Obtain through AM.
Bc	basso continuo
BCS	Bennington College Series of New Music, Bennington, Vt.
Be	Benedictus
BeW	Ludwig van Beethovens Werke. Vollständige kritisch durchgesehene überall berechtigte Ausgabe [Complete works]. 25 series. Edited by Guido Adler et al. Leipzig: Breitkopf & Härtel, [1864–1890]. Re-

	print. Ann Arbor, Michigan: J. W. Edwards, 1949.
BG	Johann Sebastian Bachs Werke [Complete works]. 61 vols in 47. Edited by the Bach-Gesellschaft. Leipzig: Breitkopf & Härtel, 1851–1926. Reprint. 60 vols in 46. Ann Arbor, Michigan: J. W. Edwards, 1947. All references in the present work are to the Breitkopf & Härtel edition above. In preparation: The new Bach-edition. 86 vols proposed. Edited by the Johann Sebastian Bach Institute, Göttingen and the Bach Archiv, Leipzig. Kassel: Bärenreiter-Verlag, 1954– .
BH	Breitkopf & Härtel, Germany. Obtain through AM.
BM	Boston Music Co., 116 Boylston St., Boston, Mass.
BoHa	Boosey and Hawkes, Oceanside, New York.
Bosworth	Bosworth. Obtain through Belwin, Rockville Centre, L.I., New York.
Broude	Broude Bros., 56 West 45th St., New York 36, N.Y.
BrW	Johannes Brahms sämtliche Werke [Complete works]. 26 vols. [Edited by H. Gál and E. Mandyczewski]. Leipzig: Breitkopf & Härtel, [1926–1927]. Reprint in preparation.
BWV	Thematisch-systematisches Verzeichnis der Musikalischen Werke von Johann Sebastian Bach [Thematic and systematic index of the musical works of Johann Sebastian Bach]. Edited by Wolfgang Schmieder. Leipzig: Breitkopf & Härtel, 1950. 747 p.
C	century
c.	circa
Casa	Casa Editrice. Obtain through WLSM.
CF	Carl Fischer, 62 Cooper Square, New York 3, N.Y.
cf	cantus firmus
Ch	Chester, J. & W., London. Obtain through Marks.
Clergé	Clergé musique sacrée, Paris. Obtain through WLSM.
Colombo	Colombo, Franco, 16 W. 61st St., New York 23, N.Y.
Con	Concordia Publishing House, 3558 South Jefferson Ave., St. Louis 18, Missouri.

xiv

Cr   Credo
Cu   Curwen and Sons, J., London. Obtain through GS.
D   Difficult. Refers to the degree of difficulty of a piece.
D   Ditson, Oliver, Boston. Obtain through Presser.
Da   David, Hans (ed). The Art of polyphonic song. New
          York: G. Schirmer, 1940. The contents are given in
          Section II, Collections, and indexed under com-
          poser.
DdT   Denkmäler deutscher Tonkunst. [1. Folge.] 65 vols.
          Edited by the Musikgeschichtlichen Kommission.
          Leipzig: Breitkopf & Härtel, 1892–1931.
Deutsch   Deutsch, Otto Erich. Schubert; thematic catalogue
          of all his works in chronological order. New York:
          W. W. Norton, n.d.
div   divisi
Dow   Dow Publishers, Inc., 134 W. 87th St., New York
          24, N.Y.
DTB   Denkmäler der Tonkunst im Bayern. 38 vols.
          Braunschweig: H. Litolff's Verlag, 1900–1938. This
          is the second series of Denkmäler deutscher Ton-
          kunst.
DTÖ   Denkmäler der Tonkunst in Österreich. 1– vols.
          Edited by Guido Adler et al. Vienna: Artaria & Co.,
          1894– . Publisher varies.
Durand   Durand et Cie, Paris. Obtain through Elkan-Vogel.
E   Easy. Refers to the degree of difficulty of a piece.
ed   editor, edited
EFL   English school of lutenist song writers. 1– vols.
          Edited by Edmund Horace Fellowes. London:
          Stainer & Bell, [1920–].
          English school of lutenist song writers. Second series.
          16 vols. Edited by Edmund Horace Fellowes. Lon-
          don: Stainer & Bell, [1925–1927]. Each series is pres-
          ently being revised and continued with Thurston
          Dart as editor under the title: The English lute
          songs.
EHG   E. Harold Geer

Elkan	Elkan-Vogel Co., 1716 Sansome St., Philadelphia 3, Penn.
Elkin	Elkin, England. Obtain through Galaxy.
E-M	Easy-medium. Refers to the degree of difficulty of a piece.
EMS	English Madrigal School. 36 vols. Edited by Edmund Horace Fellowes. London: Stainer & Bell, 1913–1924. All references in the present work are to this edition. The series is presently being revised by Thurston Dart. Many of these revisions have already appeared.
Eng	English
Enoch	Enoch, France. Obtain through AM.
eq	equal, such as equal voices
ES	E. C. Schirmer Music Co., 600 Washington St., Boston 11, Mass.
Eschig	Eschig, Max, Germany. Obtain through AM.
ESR	E. C. Schirmer, Radcliffe Choral Series, ed GWW.
ESV	E. C. Schirmer, Vassar Choral Series, ed EHG.
Eur	Europäische Madrigale für gleiche Stimmen. Edited by Egon Kraus. Zürich: Pelikan (edition 803), 1956. The contents are given in Section II, Collections, and indexed under composer.
ExRP	Expert, Henry. Répertoire populaire de la musique de la Renaissance. Paris, Senart.
Flammer	Flammer, Harold, 251 W. 19th St., New York, N.Y.
Fr	French
fr	from
Galaxy	Galaxy Music Corp., 2121 Broadway, New York 23, N.Y.
Ger	German
Gl	Gloria
GM	Geschichte der Musik in Beispielen. Edited by Arnold Schering. Leipzig: Breitkopf & Härtel, 1931. Reprint, New York: Broude, 1950. Those pieces in this collection suitable for performance by women's voices are given in Section II, Collections, as well as indexed under composers.

Gray	Gray, H. W., 159 E. 48th St., New York 17, N.Y.
GrayCMR	Gray, H. W., Church music review
GrayMS	Gray, H. W., Modern series
GS	G. Schirmer Music Co., 4 E. 49th St., New York 17, N.Y.
GWW	G. Wallace Woodworth
HAM	Historical anthology of music. Oriental, medieval and renaissance music. Edited by Archibald T. Davison and Willi Apel. Cambridge, Mass.: Harvard University Press, 1946. Those pieces in this collection suitable for performance by women's voices are given in Section II, Collections, and indexed under composer.
Hamelle	Hamelle and Co., Paris. Obtain through Presser.
HäW	Georg Friedrich Händels Werke [Complete works]. 96 vols and 6 supplements, vol 49 not published. Edited by Friedrich Chrysander. Leipzig: Breitkopf & Härtel, 1858–1902. Vols 1–18 only published by Breitkopf & Härtel. The remaining were published by Chrysander at Bergedorf bei Hamburg.
HC-L	H. Clough-Leighter
Heugel	Heugel et Cie, Paris. Obtain through Presser.
Hinrichsen	Hinrichsen, London. Obtain through P.
I	undesignated instrument
It	Italian
JF	J. Fischer and Bro., Harristown Rd., Glen Rock, N.J.
JöG	Jöde, Fritz (ed). Geistliche Lieder und Gesänge für gleiche Stimmen. Wolfenbüttel-Berlin: Georg Kallmeyer Verlag, 1930. This collection is apparently out-of-print; however it is included here due to its unusual value. It is hoped that the interested reader can locate a copy in a library. The contents are given in Section II, Collections, and indexed under composer.
JöW	Jöde, Fritz (ed). Weltliche Lieder und Gesänge für gleiche Stimmen. Wolfenbüttel-Berlin: Georg Kallmeyer Verlag, 1930. This collection is apparently

	out-of-print; however it is included here due to its unusual value. It is hoped that the interested reader can locate a copy in a library. The contents are given in Section II, Collections, and indexed under composer.
K	Köchel, Ludwig Ritter von (ed). Chronologisch-thematisches Verzeichnis sämtlicher Tonwerke Wolfgang Amade Mozart [Chronological and thematic index of the collected musical works of Wolfgang Amade Mozart]. 3d ed by Alfred Einstein with supplement by Einstein. Ann Arbor, Michigan: J. W. Edwards, 1947. 1052 p.
Kahnt	Kahnt Nachfolger, C. F., Germany. Obtain through AM.
Kalmus	Kalmus, Edwin F., 421 W. 28th St., New York 1, N.Y.
King	King Music Co., Robert, North Easton, Mass.
KKD	Katherine K. Davis
Ky	Kyrie
Lat	Latin
Leeds	Leeds Music Corp., 322 W. 48th St., New York 19, N.Y.
Legouix	Legouix, R., 4, Rue Chauveau-Legarde, 8e, Paris
Lei	Leichtentritt, Hugo (ed). Geistliche Frauenchöre alter Meister. 4 vols. Leipzig: Steingräber-Verlag, 1911. These collections may not be easily available, but are included here due to their unusual value. It is hoped that the interested reader can locate copies in a library. The contents of volumes I and II are given in Section II, Collections, and indexed under composer.
Lemoine	Lemoine et Cie, Paris. Obtain through Elkan-Vogel.
lib	library
LW	Orlando di Lassos sämtliche Werke [Complete works]. 21 vols. Edited by F. X. Haberl and Adolf Sandberger. Leipzig: Breitkopf & Härtel, [1894–1927]. This edition includes only about one-third

	of Lassus's works. All references in the present work are to the edition above. New edition: Orlando di Lasso sämtliche Werke, neue Reihe. Kassel: Bären-reiter-Verlag, 1956– .
M	Medium. Refers to the degree of difficulty of a piece.
MaO	Magnum opus musicum. A collection of 516 motets almost all of which are by Lassus.
Marks	Marks Music Corp., Edward B., 136 W. 52d St., New York 19, N.Y.
MB	Musica Britannica; a national collection of music. 19 vols continuing. London: Stainer & Bell, 1951– . References to volume IV in the present work are to the original edition (1952). There is now a revised edition of the same volume. When using the original edition, it is suggested that the reader refer to Manfred Bukofzer's review of that volume appearing in the Journal of the American Musicological Society VII (1954), p 63ff.
MCD	Music Press, Dessoff Choir Series. Ed Paul Boepple. Obtain through Presser.
M-D	Medium-difficult. Refers to the degree of difficulty of a piece.
mel	melody
Mercury	Mercury Music Corp. Obtain through Presser.
Merseberger	Merseberger Verlag, Germany. Obtain through P.
MET	Music of earlier times. Vocal and instrumental examples, 13th Century to Bach. Edited by Johannes Wolf. New York: Broude Bros., 1946. This is an American reprint of Sing- und Spielmusik aus älterer Zeit. Those pieces in this collection suitable for performance by women's voices are given in Section II, Collections, and indexed under composer.
MGA	W. A. Mozarts sämtliche Werke. Kritische durchgesehene Gesamtausgabe [Complete works]. 24 series. Edited by Johannes Brahms et al. Leipzig: Breitkopf & Härtel, 1876–1905. Reprint. Ann Arbor, Michigan: J. W. Edwards, 1951– . All refer-

	ences in the present work are to the edition above. New edition: Neue Ausgabe sämtliche Werke. Kassel: Bärenreiter-Verlag, 1955– .
Mills	Mills Music Inc., 1619 Broadway, New York, N.Y.
Möseler	Möseler Verlag, Wolfenbüttel, Germany.
MoTO	Tutte le Opere di Claudio Monteverdi [Complete works]. 16 vols. Edited by G. Francesco Malipiero. Asolo: G. Francesco Malipiero; Vienna: Universal, 1926–1942.
MP	Music Press. Obtain through Presser.
MR	McLaughlin and Reilly Co., 252 Huntington Ave., Boston, Mass.
MS	Mezzo soprano
Ms	manuscript
Musica	Musica sacra, Milan, Italy. Obtain through WLSM.
Musico	Musico, The Hague, Holland. Obtain through WLSM.
N	Novello and Co., Ltd., London. Obtain through Gray.
NCS	Novello Chorister Series. Obtain through Gray.
New	New Valley Music Press, Sage Hall, Smith College, Northampton, Mass.
no	number
Op.	opus, opera
orch	orchestra
org	organ
Ox	Oxford University Press, 147 Fifth Ave., New York 16, N.Y.
OxCS	Oxford University Press, Choral Songs
OxCSM	Oxford University Press, Choral Songs from the old masters
OxJP	Oxford University Press, The John Playford collection of vocal part music, ed W. G. Whittaker
OxOCS	Oxford University Press, Choral Songs
P	Peters, C. F., 373 Park Ave. South, New York 16, N.Y.
p	page
PAG	Frauenchor Album. Abteilung I. Edited by Göhler.

	Peters edition 2139a. The contents are given in Section II, Collections, and indexed under composer.
PAS	Frauenchor Album. Edited by Stern. Peters edition 2139. The contents are given in Section II, Collections suitable for performance, and indexed under composer.
PaW	Giovanni Pierluigi da Palestrinas Werke [Complete works]. Erste kritisch durchgesehene Gesammtausgabe. 33 vols. Edited by Th. de Witt et al. Leipzig: Breitkopf & Härtel, [1862–1907].
Peer	Peer International. Obtain through Southern.
pf	pianoforte
Presser	Presser Co., Theodore, Bryn Mawr, Penn.
PrW	Gesamtausgabe der musikalischen Werke von Michael Praetorius [Complete works]. 21 vols. Edited by Friedrich Blume. Wolfenbüttel-Berlin: Georg Kallmeyer Verlag, Möseler Verlag, 1928–1960.
Ps	psalm
pt(s)	part(s)
R	Ricordi, G. Obtain through Colombo.
Rongwen	Rongwen Music, Inc. Obtain through Broude Bros.
Rouart	Rouart, Lerolle and Co., Paris. Obtain through Colombo.
Row	Row Music Co., R. D., 725 Boylston St., Boston, Mass. Obtain through BM.
RWOM	Responses from the works of old masters. Edited by E. Harold Geer. E. C. Schirmer 869. The contents are given in Section II, Collections, and indexed under composer.
S	soprano
Sa	Sanctus
SB	Stainer and Bell, London. Obtain through Galaxy.
SbW	Franz Schuberts Werke. Kritische durchgesehene Gesamtausgabe [Complete works]. 21 vols and Revisionsbericht. Edited by Johannes Brahms et al. Leipzig: Breitkopf & Härtel, 1884–1897.
Schott	Schott Söhne, Germany. Obtain through AM.

ScW	Heinrich Schütz's sämtliche Werke [Complete works]. 18 vols. Edited by Philipp Spitta, A. Schering, Heinrich Spitta. Leipzig: Breitkopf & Härtel, [1885–1927]. All references in the present work are to this edition. New edition: Neue Ausgabe sämtliche Werke. 30 vols proposed. Kassel: Bärenreiter-Verlag, 1955– .
Senart	Senart, Maurice, Paris. Obtain through Colombo.
Simrock	Simrock, N., Germany. Obtain through AM.
SmW	Robert Schumann's Werke [Complete works]. Edited by Clara Schumann. 14 vols. Leipzig: Breitkopf & Härtel, 1881–1893.
Southern	Southern Music Publishing Co., Inc., 1619 Broadway, New York 19, N.Y.
Ste	Stevens, Georgia (ed). Mediaeval and renaissance choral music for equal voices a cappella. Boston: McLaughlin and Reilly Co., 1940. The contents are given in Section II, Collections, and indexed under composer.
Summy	Summy-Birchard Co., 1834 Ridge Ave., Evanston, Ill.
SWV	Schütz-Werke-Verzeichnis [Index of Schütz's works]. Edited by Werner Bittinger. Kassel: Bärenreiter, 1960. 191 p.
SwW	Werken van Jan Pieterszn. Sweelinck [Complete works]. 12 vols in 10. Edited by the Vereeniging voor Noord-Nederlands Muziekgeschiedenis. Leipzig: Breitkopf & Härtel, 1894–1901.
T	tenor
T:	text, author, or source
Tischner	Tischner und Jagenberg, Köln am Rhein, Germany.
Tov	Tovey, Donald (ed). Laudate pueri. Sacred music of the XVIth century [sic]. London: Augener, 1910. Each title of this collection is also available separately. The contents are given in Section II, Collections, and indexed under composer.
trans	translated or translation
U	Universal edition. Obtain through Presser except as indicated within *List*.

unac	unaccompanied
UPC	University of Pennsylvania Choral Series. The Association of American Choruses. Drinker Library of Choral Music. The Free Library of Philadelphia, Philadelphia 3, Penn.
Valley	Valley Music Press, see New Valley Music Press
vio	violin(s)
ViW	Thomas Ludovici Victoria Abulensis Opera Omnia [Complete works]. 8 vols. Edited by Philippo Pedrell. Leipzig: Breitkopf & Härtel, 1902–1913.
vol(s)	volume(s)
vrs	verse or verses
W	M. Witmark & Sons, Music Publishers Holding Corp., Standard and Educational Div., 488 Madison Ave., New York, N.Y.
w/	with
Wellesley	Wellesley College, Music Department, Wellesley, Mass.
Whit	Whittaker, W. Gillies (ed). The Oxford graduated round book. Oxford University Press, 1937. The complete contents are given in Section II, Collections suitable for performance. Items by Beethoven, Haydn, Mozart and Schubert are indexed under composer.
Williams	Williams, Jos., London. Obtain through Mills.
WLSM	World Library of Sacred Music, 1846 Westwood Ave., Cincinnati 14, Ohio.
WMtH	Witmark and Sons, Mt. Holyoke Choral Series, ed Clara Tillinghast. Obtain through W.
WoO	Werke ohne Opuszahl [Works without opus number]. Designations for works of Beethoven are those given in Das Werk Beethovens thematische-bibliographisches Verzeichnis . . . von Georg Kinsky. Munich-Duisburg, 1955. 808 p.
Wood	Wood, B. F. Obtain through Mills.
WW	Wilson, Philip and Peter Warlock
Z	Zwölf geistliche Chöre, edited by G. Dessoff. Schott. Obtain through AM.

SECTION ONE

Catalog by Composers

ADAM DE LA HALLE C. 1237–1287

A Dieu confie amourettes   SSA unac 1:30 E;   in Rondeaux, Salabert

A jointes mains vous dois   SSA unac 0:45 E-M;   in Rondeaux, Salabert

Amour et ma dame aussi   SSA unac 1:00 E;   in Rondeaux, Salabert

Bonne amourette   SSA unac 0:45 E;   in Rondeaux, Salabert

Dame, suis trahi   SSA unac 1:45 E;   in Rondeaux, Salabert

Dieu, comment pourroie   SSA unac 1:00 E-M;   in Rondeaux, Salabert

Dieu soit en cette maison   SSA unac 1:30 E;   in Rondeaux, Salabert

Le doux regard de ma dame [1st version]   SSA unac 1:30 E; in Rondeaux, Salabert

Le doux regard de ma dame [2d version]   SSA unac 1:30 E; in Rondeaux, Salabert

Fi, mari, de votre amour   SSA unac 0:45 E-M;   in Rondeaux, Salabert

Fines amourettes j'ai   SSA unac 1:15 E-M;   in Rondeaux, Salabert

Haro, le mal d'aimer [1st version]   SSA unac 1:00 E;   in Rondeaux, Salabert

Haro, le mal d'aimer [2d version]   SSA unac 0:45 E;   in Rondeaux, Salabert

Hé, Dieu, quand verrai   SSA unac 0:45 E-M;   in Rondeaux, Salabert

Je meurs, je meurs d'amourette   SSA unac 1:00 E;   in Rondeaux, Salabert

Or est Bayard en la pâture   SSA unac 1:30 M;   in Rondeaux, Salabert

Rondeaux à 3 voix égales (see individual titles for complete information);   La Musique française au Moyen-âge, Salabert
  Je meurs, je meurs d'amourette / Le doux regard de ma dame / Haro! le mal d'aimer / Fines amourettes j'ai / A Dieu confie amourettes / Dame, suis trahi / Amour, et ma dame aussi / Or est Bayard en la pâture / A jointes mains vous dois / Fi, mari, de votre amour / Hé, Dieu, quand

verrai / Dieu, comment pourroie / Trop désire à revoir / Bonne amourette / Tant que je vivrai / Dieu soit en cette maison.

Tant que je vivrai   SSA unac 1:00 E-M;   in Rondeaux, Salabert

Trop désire à revoir   SSA unac 1:00 E-M;   in Rondeaux, Salabert

AGAZZARI, AGOSTINO 1578–1640
Jubilate Deo   T: Ps XCVI   AA org 0:45x2 0:30x2 E-M; ed Arnold Klaes, Schott Canticum vetus

AGOSTINI, PAOLO c. 1580–1629
Adoramus te, Christe   SSAA unac 1:20 M;   in Tov, p 28

AICHINGER, GREGOR 1564–1628
Assumpta est Maria   SSA unac 2:00 M;   WMtH 2W2899; ed Damrosch, GS 6250;   in Lei I, 12

Ave Regina coelorum, in DTB X, p 53   SSA unac 3:00 M; Lat Ger (Ave, der Himmel Königin) in JöG, p 92;   in Lei I, 14

Regina coeli   SSA unac 4:00 E-M;   WMtH 2900

Salve Regina   SST (A) unac 2:45 E-M;   Bank

ALBERT, HEINRICH 1604–1651
Das Leid ist hier   T: Simon Dach   SSA unac 0:45x2 M; in JöG, p 110

Der Nordwind lässt sich hören [not the original text], in DdT XII, p 25 w/original text, Die Sonn' ist abgegangen   SSA unac 0:30 E-M;   0:30x3 in JöW, p 61

Die Sonne rennt mit Prangen   T: Simon Dach   SSA unac 0:25x2 E-M;   in JöW, p 37

ANDREWS, H. K. 1904–
Evening service: Magnificat [and] Nunc dimittis—My soul doth magnify the Lord   SSASSA org 4:00 1:30 E;   Ox Church music 487

ANDRIESSEN, HENDRIK 1892–
O Lord, with wondrous mystery   T: Michael Gannon   3 eq org ad lib. 0:40x2 E;   WLSM

Animuccia, Giovanni c. 1500–1571
  Kyrie [based on Conditor alme siderum]   SSAA unac 4:00
    E-M;   in Ste, p 38

Anonymous
  Abide, I hope it be the best [15th C]   SAT (A) unac 1:00 E;
    w/I rede that thou be jolly and glad [solo], in SB Fayrfax 5
    and 6
  The Agincourt song [14th-C English carol], in MB IV, p 6—
    Deo gracias   SA (transposition necessary) unac 0:10 0:10x5
    0:40x4 M;   w/To many, in SB Mediaeval carols 2
  Ah, man, assay [14th-C English carol], in MB IV, p 12   SA
    w/fa-burden (transposition necessary) unac 0:15x7 0:15x6 M;
    w/Goday, Of a rose, in SB Mediaeval carols 4
  Alas, departing is ground of woe   T: Anon, c. 1440   SA
    unac 1:10 E;   SB Fayrfax 7
  All creatures now rejoice [early 17th C], fr British Museum Addi-
    tional Ms 34800   SSA unac 2:00 E;   ed Warlock, OxCSM
    372
  Alleluia. Angelus Domini [fr Chartres end of 11th C]   SS
    unac 1:00 E;   in Ste, p 2
  Alleluia: Diva natalicia [14th-C English carol], in MB IV, p 21
    SA (transposition necessary) unac 0:20x4 0:20x3 M;   w/Te
    Deum, in SB Mediaeval carols 11
  Alleluia: Now may we mirthës make [14th-C English carol],
    in MB IV, p 94   SAA (transposition necessary) unac 0:10x4
    0:10x4 0:50x3 M;   w/Now, in SB Mediaeval carols 3
  Alleluia-Psallat, fr Worcester mediaeval harmony, XIII? C   T:
    based on Ps CL   SSA unac 1:20 E;   in Ste, p 10
  Alma redemptoris mater [14th-C English carol], in MB IV, p 3
    SA w/fa-burden (transposition necessary) unac 0:15x6 0:30x5
    M;   w/Hail, Nowell: In Bethlem, in SB Mediaeval carols 1
  Angelus ad Virginem (Gabriel and Mary) [14th C]—Angelus ad
    Virginem (Gabriel from heaven's King)   SSA unac 0:45x2
    M;   ed Denis Stevens w/Anon, Qui creavit, in N Trios 609
  Angelus ad Virginem (The Annunciation carol) [13th C English]
    —Angelus ad Virginem / Gabriel, from ev'ne sing (Gabriel,

5

Por la puente Juana que no por el agua [Spanish 16th C]
SAT (A if cadential D's are turned up) unac 1:00 E;   in
MET, p 100

Proface, welcome [14th-C English carol], in MB IV, p 96
SAA unac 0:30x5 0:30x4 M;   w/Lullay: I saw, in SB Mediaeval carols 10

Puellare gremium, fr Worcester Mediaeval Harmony, 13th? C
SSA unac 2:00 E;   in Ste, p 5

Qui creavit coelum (He who made the starry skies) [15th C]
SSA unac 0:30x4 E;   ed Denis Stevens w/Angelus, in N Trios
609

Saint Thomas honour we [14th C English carol], in MB IV, p 48
SSA (transposition necessary) unac 0:15 0:15x8 0:45x7 M;
w/Nowell: Tidings, in SB Mediaeval carols 8

Salve virgo nobilis Maria [13th C]   TTT (SSS) unac 1:20
E-M;   in MET, p 6

Te Deum [14th-C English carol], in MB IV, p 83   SA w/fa-
burden (transposition necessary) unac 0:30x4 0:30x3 M;
w/Alleluia: Diva, in SB Mediaeval carols 11

To many a well [14th-C English carol], in MB IV, p 104   SAA
(transposition necessary) unac 0:30x4 0:20x4 1:00x3 M;
w/Agincourt, in SB Mediaeval carols 2

Tröst mich, mein Lieb, fr a parchment Ms in the British Museum [16th C]   SSA unac 1:00 E-M;   in JöW, p 81

Vergine bella;   see Laude

Wenn meine Suend' mich kraenken (When o'er my sins I sorrow) [16th C]   T: ascribed to Justus Gesenius 1601–1673
SSA unac 1:00x2 E;   ed Bangert and Rosel, Eng only, Con
98–1252

What tidings bringest thou? [14th C English carol], in MB IV,
p 8   SAA unac 0:20x4 0:40x3 M;   w/Nowell sing, Nova,
in SB Mediaeval carols 7

Wohlauf, ihr lieben Gsellen   SSA unac 0:30x3 E;   in JöW,
p 51

Young men and maidens [canon]   SSA unac 1:00 E;   w/Nor-
ris: I said, Webbe: Glory, Hayes: Alleluia, in SB Part
song 85

APIARIUS, MATTHAIS 1500–1553
Es taget vor dem Walde   SA unac 1:00x2 E;   in JöW, p 18

ARCADELT, JACQUES 1510?–1557?
Ave Maria;   This composition is an arrangement of Nous voyons que les hommes (printed in The Chansons of Jacques Arcadelt. Edited by Everett B. Helm. Smith College Music Archives V.) See Scholes, Misattributed Compositions, in Oxford Companion to Music;   also Gustave Reese, Music in the Renaissance.
Voi mi ponest' in foco (Du hast mein Herz entzündet)   SSA unac 1:00 E-M;   in GM, p 96

ARNE, DR. THOMAS A 1710–1778
Beside a lake [not the original text]   T: Clifford Bax   SSA unac 3:00 E-M;   SB Part song 89
Help me O Lord [canon]   SSA unac 0:45 E;   w/Byrd, Benedictus, in SB Church choir lib 28

ARRIEU, CLAUDE 1903–
L'Été—Je suis l'Été vainqueur   T: J. Lallemand 3 or 4 eq, S solo ad lib. pf ad lib.;   Lemoine 22766

ATTWOOD, THOMAS 1765–1838
Songs of praise the angels sang   T: James Montgomery SS pf 2:00x2 E;   NCS 27

BACH, JOHANN SEBASTIAN 1685–1750
Ach Herr, mein Gott, vergib mir's doch (Ah, Lord, my God, forgive Thou me), fr Cantata 113 Herr Jesu Christ, du höchstes Gut, in BG XXIV, p 76   T: after hymn of Bartholomäus Ringwaldt, 1588   SA Bc 2:50 M;   Eng only in Eighteen, UPC 6A;   Eng Ger, MCD 27
Die Armut, so Gott auf sich nimmt (A pauper our Lord chose to be), fr Cantata 91 Gelobet seist du, Jesu Christ, in BG XXII, p 26   T: Martin Luther   SA orch (pf) 1:45x2 1:45 M;   Eng only in Eighteen, UPC 6A
Beruft Gott selbst, so muss der Segen (Call ye on God, so gain His blessing), fr Cantata 88 Siehe, ich will viel Fischer aussen-

den, in BG XX (1), p 172   SA orch (pf) 5:15 M;   Eng only in Eighteen, UPC 6A

Denn das Gesetz des Geistes (Thus then, the law of the Spirit), fr Jesu, meine Freude [BWV 227], in BG XXXIV, p 67 SSA unac 1:10 M;   ed Damrosch Eng only, GS 7604

Domine Deus, fr G Mass [BWV 236], in BG VIII, p 188   SA orch (pf) 4:00 M;   in Eighteen, UPC 6A

Eighteen duets for soprano and alto from the cantatas (see individual titles for origin, BG, specific texts, timings and grades);   Eng only (except Domine Deus, Lat only) trans and ed Henry S. Drinker, accompaniments missing but available from publisher, UPC 6A;   same as UPC 6A except missing Domine Deus, UPC 6

> Den Tod niemand zwingen kunnt / Nun komm, der Heiden Heiland / Herr Gott Vater, mein starker Held / Er kennt die rechten Freudenstunden / Gedenk an Jesu bittern Tod / Ich folge dir nach / Nimm mich mir und gib mich dir / Herr, du siehst statt guter Werke / Weichet, weichet, Furcht und Schrecken / Ihr klaget mit Seufzen, ich jauchze mit Schall / Wir eilen mit schwachen, doch emsigen Schritten / Beruft Gott selbst, so muss der Segen / Die Armut, so Gott auf sich nimmt / Wenn des Kreuzes Bitterkeiten / Ach Herr, mein Gott, vergib mirs doch / Entziehe dich eilends, mein Herze, der Welt / Herz, zerreiss des Mammons Kette / Domine Deus, agnus Dei.

Entziehe dich eilends, mein Herze, der Welt (Away now, my heart, haste away from the world), fr Cantata 124 Meinen Jesum lass' ich nicht, in BG XXVI, p 78   T: after hymn of Christian Keimann, 1658   SA Bc 1:40x2 1:10 M;   Eng only in Eighteen, UPC 6A

Er kennt die rechten Freudenstunden (He knows the time when joy is seemly), fr Cantata 93 Wer nur den lieben Gott lässt walten, in BG XXII, p 87   T: George Neumark, 1657 SA orch (pf) 0:45x2 0:45 M;   Eng only in Eighteen, UPC 6A

Et misericordia (And His mercy), fr Magnificat [BWV 243], in BG XI, p 37   AT orch (pf) 3:10 M;   ed Whittaker, transposed for SA OxCSM 1439

Gedenk an Jesu bittern Tod (Remember Jesus' bitter death),

fr Cantata 101 Nimm von uns, Herr, du treuer Gott, in BG XXIII, p 27   T: Martin Moller, 1584   SA orch (pf) 4:00 M;   Eng only in Eighteen, UPC 6A

Herr, du siehst statt guter Werke (Lord, with Thee our works awaken), fr Cantata 9 Es ist das Heil uns kommen her, in BG I, p 266   T: after hymn of Paul Speratus, 1524   SA orch (pf) 1:50x2 0:30 M;   Eng only in Eighteen, UPC 6A

Herr Gott Vater, mein starker Held (Lord God, our Father, mighty Lord), fr Cantata 37 Wer da glaubet und getauft wird, in BG VII, p 272   T: Philipp Nicolai, 1599   SA Bc 2:00 M;   Eng only in Eighteen, UPC 6A

Der Herr segne euch (The Lord bless you), fr Cantata 196 Der Herr denket an uns, in BG XIII, p 82   T: Ps CXV: 13–15 TB orch (pf) 1:45 M;   ed Bunjes, transposed for SA, Con 98–1474

Herz, zereiss des Mammons Kette (Rend, my heart, the chains of Mammon), fr Cantata 168 Tue Rechnung! Donnerwort, in BG XXXIII, p 163   T: Salomo Franck, 1715   SA Bc 2:00 M;   Eng only in Eighteen, UPC 6A

Ich folge dir nach (I follow Thee still), fr Cantata 159 Sehet, wir geh'n hinauf gen Jerusalem, in BG XXXII, p 160   T: Paul Gerhardt and Picander   SA orch (pf) 4:00 M;   Eng only in Eighteen, UPC 6A

Ihr klaget mit Seufzen, ich jauchze mit Schall (I'm laughing and shouting with loudest acclaim), fr Cantata 15 Denn du wirst meine Seele nicht in der Hölle lassen, in BG II, p 160 SA orch (pf) 2:00 M;   Eng only in Eighteen, UPC 6A

Nimm mich mir und gib mich dir (Take Thou me thine own to be), fr Cantata 163 Nun jedem das Seine, in BG XXXIII, p 61   T: Salomo Franck, 1715   SA orch (pf) 4:00 M; Eng only in Eighteen, UPC 6A

Nun komm, der Heiden Heiland (Come Thou, of man the Saviour), fr Cantata 36 Schwingt freudig euch empor, in BG VII, p 236   SA orch (pf) 2:10 M;   Eng only in Eighteen, UPC 6A;   Eng Ger, MCD 26

Suscepit Israel (His servant Israel), fr Magnificat [BWV 243], in BG XI, p 54   SSA 2 oboes, Bc (org) 2:10 M-D;   ed HC-L ESR 813;   ESV 850;   Bank K 48

Den Tod niemand zwingen kunnt (Oh death, none could thee subdue), fr Cantata 4 Christ lag in Todesbanden, in BG I, p 110   T: Martin Luther   SA orch (pf) 2:10 M;   Eng only in Eighteen, UPC 6A

Weichet, weichet, Furcht und Schrecken (Vanish fear and terror), fr Cantata 15 Denn du wirst meine Seele nicht in der Hölle lassen, in BG II, p 139   SA orch (pf) 2:15x2 0:40 M; Eng only in Eighteen, UPC 6A

Wenn des Kreuzes Bitterkeiten (Whoso bears his load unbending), fr Cantata 99 Was Gott tut, das ist wohlgetan, in BG XXII, p 272   T: after hymn of Samuel Rodigast, 1676 SA orch (pf) 2:40 M;   Eng only in Eighteen, UPC 6A

Wir eilen mit schwachen, doch emsigen Schritten (We hasten with eager, yet faltering footsteps), fr Cantata 78 Jesu, der du meine Seele, in BG XVIII, p 269   T: after hymn of Johann Rist, 1621   SA Bc 1:45x2 1:40 M;   Eng only in Eighteen, UPC 6A;   ed Talmadge, ES 2506;   Galaxy 904

BACON, ERNST 1898–

The birds—Says the robin as she flew   SA pf 1:10 E;   Rongwen 283

Chop-cherry—Thou gav'st me to kisse   T: Robert Herrick SSA pf 1:00 E;   in Seven canons, MP 114

From Emily's diary, secular cantata of 10 choral and 2 instrumental pieces which may be performed together or separately T: Emily Dickinson   SSAA, SA solo pf (small orch) E-M; GS 1879

Preface [instrumental] 1:40 / My river runs to thee [chorus] 1:15 / I dwell in Possibility [S solo] 2:15 / A drop fell on the apple tree [chorus and S solo] 0:50 / The daisy follows soft the sun [chorus] 3:00 / What soft, cherubic creatures [chorus] 1:00 / Our share of night to bear [chorus] 1:00 / When roses cease to bloom, dear [A solo] 1:45 / It's coming [chorus] 2:15 / "Unto me?" [chorus and SA duet] 3:45 / Not what we did shall be the test [chorus] 2:10 / Afterthought [instrumental] 1:10.

The little children—Upon the little children of the schools   T: fr the Talmud   SA pf 0:40 E;   in Seven canons, MP 114

The pelican—O a wonderful bird is the pelican   2 eq pf 1:00
　　M;　in Seven canons, MP 114

Precepts of Angelus Silesius   T: Johann Scheffer, 1624–1677,
　　trans Paul Carus   3–6 women's voices unac M-D;   BCS 4
　　　Prologue—Two eyes our souls possess 0:30 / Chorale—
　　　Thou needst not cry to God 0:20 / Sermon—God never did
　　　exist 1:10 / Ground—Dost think, poor man 1:00 / Air—
　　　The rose is without why 0:40 / Drone—Rain rains not for
　　　itself 1:00 / Chorale—All creatures are the voice 0:30 / Song
　　　—The nightingale will not 1:00 / Response—"Where is
　　　my residence?" 1:30 / Conclusion—Friend, it is now enough
　　　1:45.

Schools and rules—Thank God! I never was sent to school   T:
　　William Blake   4 eq pf 1:00 E-M;   in Seven canons, MP 114

Seven canons (see individual titles for complete information);
　　MP 114
　　　God [SATB] / Sinai [SAB] / Schools and rules [4 eq] / The
　　　pelican [2 eq] / The little children [SA] / Chopcherry [SA] /
　　　Money [STB].

Water—The water understands civilization well   T: R. W.
　　Emerson   SA pf (org) 1:15 M;   Galaxy GMC 2169

BAINI, GIUSEPPE 1775–1844
　　Beata mortui   SSA, SSA soli pf 2:00 E;   Z, no 2

BAINI, LORENZO 18th C
　　Caro mea   SSA unac 2:15 E;   Z, no 1

BARBER, SAMUEL 1910–
　　A nun takes the veil—I have desired to go where spring never
　　　fails [a choral setting by the composer of his solo song Op. 13,
　　　no. 1]   T: Gerald Manley Hopkins   SSAA unac 1:30
　　　E-M;   GS 10860
　　The virgin martyrs [Op. 8]—Therefore come they   T: Helen
　　　Waddell after Sigebert of Gembloux   SSA unac 3:30 M;
　　　GS 8386

BARTLET, JOHN flourished c. 1606–1610
　　Fortune, love and time, in EFL Bartlet, p 26   SS lute (pf)
　　　0:40x2 0:20 M;   SB LU 24

Whither runneth my sweetheart?, in EFL Bartlet, p 30   SS
lute (pf) 0:30 0:30x2 E;   W 2805

BARTÓK, BÉLA 1881–1945
Breadbaking—Down below my garden yonder   T: trans Elizabeth Herzog   SA unac or orch 2:10 M;   BoHa 1669
Don't leave me—Do not go   T: trans Elizabeth Herzog   SA unac or orch 1:30 E-M;   BoHa 1668
Enchanting song—Forth let the cattle roam   T: trans Nancy Bush   SSA unac 1:15 M-D;   BoHa 1954
Hussar—Round this town   T: trans Elizabeth Herzog   SA unac or orch 1:45 M;   BoHa 1673
Lad's dance (Burschentanz)   T: trans Martin Lindsay   SSAA orch (pf ad lib.) 3:30 D;   Slovak Hungarian Ger Eng (score) Ger Eng (voice parts) w/Wedding, Lullaby, in U (obtain USA fr BoHa)
Loafer—Sunday you sip brandy   T: trans Elizabeth Herzog   SSA unac or orch 0:40 M;   BoHa 1671
Lullaby (Wiegenlied)   T: trans Martin Lindsay   SSAA orch (pf ad lib.) 4:30 D;   Slovac Hungarian Ger Eng (score) Ger Eng (voice parts) w/Wedding, Lad's, in U (obtain USA fr BoHa)
Mocking of youth—Oh, a girl is costly   T: trans Nancy Bush   SSA unac 0:57 M;   BoHa 1955
Only tell me   T: trans Elizabeth Herzog   SA unac or orch 1:50 (unac) 2:40 (w/orch) M;   BoHa 1670
Spring—Soft the swallow twitters   T: trans Nancy Bush   SSA unac 2:00 M;   BoHa 1953
Teasing song—Lasses cost a fortune   T: trans Elizabeth Herzog   SSA unac or orch 1:00 (unac) 1:10 (w/orch) M;   BoHa 1672
Wedding (Hochzeit)   T: trans Martin Lindsay   SSA orch (pf ad lib.) 6:15 D;   Slovak Hungarian Ger Eng (score) Ger Eng (voice parts) w/Lullaby, Lad's, in U (obtain USA fr BoHa)
Wooing of a girl—Tell my why you come and go   T: trans Nancy Bush   SSA unac 1:37 M;   BoHa 1956

BASILI, ANDREA 1720–1775 or 1777
Ave Rex noster   SSA unac 1:45 M;   Z, no 3

BASILI, FRANCESCO 1767–1850
Christus factus est   SSA unac;   Z, no 4

BATESON, THOMAS c. 1570–1630
The nightingale in silent night, in EMS XXII, p 36   SSAA
unac 0:30 0:20x2 E-M;   SB M 22/8

BEETHOVEN, LUDWIG VAN 1770–1827
An Mälzel (To Mälzel) [canon] [WoO 162], in BeW XXXIII,
p 177—(Tick-a-tack, dear old Mälzel)   T: trans Albert G.
Latham   4 eq 1:30 E-M;   Eng only, in Whit, p 16
Ars longa (Art is long) [canon] [WoO 192], not in BeW   T:
trans Albert G. Latham   4 eq 0:30 E;   in Whit, p 13
Ewig dein (I am thine) [canon] [WoO 161], in BeW XXXIII,
p 198   T: adapted Albert G. Latham   3 eq 1:00 E;   Eng
only, in Whit, p 9
Glück (Fortune) [canon] [WoO 171], not in BeW   T: trans
Albert G. Latham   4 eq 0:30 E;   in Whit, p 15
Im Arm der Liebe ruht sich's wohl (If love's arm hold thee)
[canon] [WoO 159], in BeW XXXIII, p 176   T: trans
Albert G. Latham   3 eq 0:30 E;   Eng only, in Whit, p 10

BENNET, JOHN c. 1570–1614
Cruel unkind, in EMS XXIII, p 51   SSAA unac 1:00 E-M
I wander up and down, in EMS XXIII, p 1   SSAA unac 1:15
E;   SB M 23/1
Weep, silly soul disdained, in EMS XXIII, p 6   SSAA unac
0:15 1:15x2 E-M;   SB M 23/2

BERGSMA, WILLIAM 1921–
Let true love among us be   T: 13th C anon., trans Nancy
Nickerson   SA pf 2:00 M;   CF CM 6534

BERLIOZ, HECTOR 1803–1869
(Ophelia) [Op. 18, no 2]—(Ophelia, all distraught)   SA orch
(pf) 5:45 M;   trans Troutbeck, Eng only, N Trios 248
Prière du Matin [Op. 19, no 4]—O père qu'adore mon père   T:
A. de Lamartine   SA pf 0:45x2 E-M;   N Trios 808

Veni, Creator Spiritus   SSA, SSA soli org ad lib. 2:40 M;
AJ 13;   BH 1679

BEVERIDGE, THOMAS 1938–
Fellowschipe—Lo, here is fellowschipe   T: Florence Converse
SSA pf 1:15 E-M;   ES 2533
O cool is the valley now   T: James Joyce   SSA pf 1:50
E-M;   ES 2523
O fanciulla qui fai (Oh fresh young girl)   T: Giovanni Prati,
trans Victoria Glaser   SSA, S solo pf 4:30 M;   ES 2522

BILLINGS, WILLIAM 1746–1800
When Jesus wept [round]   T: fr New England Psalm Singer,
1770   four eq unac 2:00 E;   Mercury MC 102

BINCHOIS, GILLES DE C. 1400–1467
A solis ortus cardine (From where the rising sun ascends)   SSA
unac 1:00x4 E-M;   Eng included, not underlayed, MCD 38
Files à marier   SSII 1:15 E-M;   in HAM, p 74

BLANDFORD, MARQUIS OF 1738–1817
Cherry-stones—Tinker, tailor, soldier, sailor   T: Clifford Bax,
not the original text   SSA unac 0:45x2 M;   SB Part song
101

BODA, JOHN 1922–
Before the paling of the stars   T: Christina Georgina Rossetti,
1830–1894   SA pf 4:10 E;   Con 98–1566

BODENSCHATZ, ERHARD 1576–1636
De passione—Sanguis Jesu Christi   SA unac 1:00 E-M;   in
GM, p 171

BOLOGNA, see JACOPO DA BOLOGNA

BOULANGER, LILI 1893–1918
Les sirènes [1911]—Nous sommes la beauté   T: Ch. Grand-
mougin   SST(A), S solo pf 5:00 E-M;   R Société anonyme
32

BOYCE, WILLIAM 1710–1779
Allelujah [canon]   SSA unac 1:00 E;   ed Holst w/Boyce:
Glory, Anon.:   As pants, Webbe: Who can, in SB Part song
45

Glory be to God on high [canon]   SSA unac 1:45 E;   ed
Holst w/Boyce: Alleluja, Anon.:   As pants, Webbe: Who
can, in SB Part song 45

Remember, O Lord, fr Lord thou hast been our refuge   SSA
org 4:00 M;   N 92

The sorrows of my heart are enlarged   T: Ps XXV: 17–18
SA pf 1:10 M;   Con 98–1380

BRAHMS, JOHANNES 1833–1897

Op. 12 Ave Maria, gratia plena, in BrW XIX, p 113   SSAA
org (orch) 5:00 D;   P 3651;   Lat Eng (Father almighty, O
hear us) GS 9115;   Eng only (Blessed are they that dwell in
Thy house)   T: Ps LXXXIV: 4, 8, 9 org, N Chorister 2;
Eng only (Blessed are they that dwell in Thy house)   T: Ps
LXXXIV: 4, 8, 9 pf, ES 2515

Op. 17 Gesänge für Frauenchor (Songs for women's chorus), in
BrW XIX, p 135–152

no 1 Es tönt ein voller Harfenklang   T: Ruperti   SSA
horn, harp (pf) 4:00 M;   Ger Eng (Whene're the sounding harp is heard) trans Troutbeck, in Four trios (Op. 17,
1–4) N;   N Trios 180;   Eng only (I hear a harp) trans
Natalia Macfarren, I pts available, GS 4300;   ed HC-L
Eng only (I hear a harp) trans Natalia Macfarren, I pts
available, ES 494

no 2 Lied von Shakespeare's Twelfth night   SSA 2 horns,
harp (pf) 2:30 M;   Ger Eng (Come away death) in Four
trios (Op. 17, 1–4) N;   N Trios 181;   Eng only (Come
away death), I pts available, GS 4301;   Eng only (Come
away death), I pts available, ES 2504

no 3 Der Gärtner—Wohin ich geh' und schaue   T: Eich-
endorff   SSA 2 horns, harp (pf) 1:45x2 M;   Ger Eng
(The gardener—Whene're my footsteps wander) trans
Troutbeck in Four trios (Op. 17, 1–4) N;   N Trios 182;
Eng only (Greetings—Whene're I look or wander) trans
Natalia Mcfarren, I pts available, ES 2503;   Eng only
(Greetings—Whene're I look or wander) trans Natalia
Mcfarren, I pts available, GS 4302

no 4 Gesang aus Fingal—Wein' an den Felsen T: Ossian
SSA 2 horns, harp (pf) 5:50 M; Ger Eng (The death of
Trenar—Weep on the rocks) trans Troutbeck, in Four
trios (Op. 17, 1–4) N; N Trios 183; Eng only (Song
of Ossian's Fingal—Weep on the rocks), I pts available,
GS 29; Eng only (Song of Ossian's Fingal—Weep on the
rocks), I pts available, GS 4303; ed HC-L Eng only
(Song of Ossian's Fingal—Weep on the rocks), I pts available, ES 495

Op. 20 Drei Duette (Three duets), in BrW XXII, p 1–16
no 1 Weg der Liebe [part 1]—Über die Berge T: Johann
Gottfried von Herder SA pf 3:00 M; Ger Eng (Over
the billows) trans KKD, ES 1529; Ger Eng (Over the
oceans) trans Paul England, N 132

no 2 Weg der Liebe [part 2]—Den gordischen Knoten T:
Johann Gottfried von Herder SA pf 2:00 M; ed
HC-L Eng only (The voice of the morn) trans Florence
Hoare, ES 440

no 3 Die Meere—Alle Winde schlafen SA pf 0:50x2 M;
Ger Eng (The sea—Evening winds are sleeping), in Concord song book, series 17–18, ES

Op. 27 Der 13. Psalm—Herr, wie lange willst du mein so gar
vergessen (How long, O Lord, will thou forget me), in BrW
XX, p 1 SSA org 5:30 D; Au 13540; Eng only GS 174;
Eng only, Hinrichsen 42

Op. 37 Drei geistliche Chöre (Three sacred choruses), in BrW
XXI, p 159
no 1 O bone Jesu (Father eternal) SSAA unac 1:10 M-D;
in Three sacred choruses (Op. 37) Broude 136; N 429

no 2 Adoramus te, Christe (We adore Thee Christ) SSAA
unac 1:40 M-D; in Three sacred choruses (Op. 37)
Broude 136; Lat only, in JöG, p 89

no 3 Regina coeli (O Queen of Heaven) SSAA, SA solo
unac 2:45 M-D; in Three sacred choruses (Op. 37)
Broude 136; (Be joyful Queen of the heavens) N 431

Op. 44 Zwölf Lieder und Romanzen (Twelve songs and ro-
mances), in BrW XXI, p 164–178 SSA pf ad lib.
no 1 Minnelied (Love song)—Der Holdseligen sonder

Wank T: Johann Heinrich Voss 0:15x4 M-D; in
P 3669a (Op. 44, 1–6); Ger Eng (To the fairest without
delay) N 333; Ger Eng (To the fairest without delay)
ES 1070; Ger Eng (Ah! how sweet is the maid I love)
Kalmus; Eng only (To my darling one strong and gay)
pf missing, in UPC 72 (Op. 44, 1, 3, 4, 5)

no 2 Der Bräutigam (The bridegroom)—Von allen Berge
nieder T: Eichendorff 0:25x2 1:00 M-D; in P 3669a
(Op. 44, 1–6); Ger Eng (From every lofty mountain)
Kalmus; ed HC-L Ger Eng (From all the snow-capped
mountains) ES 1068; Eng only (From every mountain
sounding) pf missing, in UPC 73 (Op. 44, 2, 7, 9)

no 3 Barkarole (Barcarolle)—O Fischer auf den Fluten
0:35x5 M; in P 3669a (Op. 44, 1–6); Ger Eng (O fisher
on the waters) N 335; ed HC-L Ger Eng (O fisher on
the water) ES 1069; Eng only trans George L. Osgood
(O fisher on the water) D 4790; Eng only (O fisherman
come hither) pf missing, in UPC 72 (Op. 44, 1, 3, 4, 5);
Ger Eng (O fisher on the ocean) Kalmus

no 4 Fragen (Questionings)—Wozu ist mein langes Haar
dann 0:45 M-D; in P 3669a (Op. 44, 1–6); Eng only
(O why have I long and curly hair) pf missing, in UPC 72
(Op. 44, 1, 3, 4, 5)

no 5 Die Müllerin (The miller's daughter)—Die Mühle,
die dreht ihre Flügel T: Chamisso 0:20x3 M-D; in
P 3669a (Op. 44, 1–6); Ger Eng (The windmill its sails
is swift turning) Kalmus; Eng only (The sails of the
windmill are sweeping) pf missing, in UPC 72 (Op. 44,
1, 3, 4, 5)

no 6 Die Nonne (The nun)—Im stillen Klostergarten T:
L. Uhland 0:30x3 M-D; in P 3669a (Op. 44, 1–6); Ger
Eng (Within the covent garden) Kalmus

no 7 Nun stehn die Rosen in Blüte T: Paul Heyse
0:25x3 M; in P 3669b (Op. 44, 7–12); Ger Eng (Now
all the roses are blooming) ES 1072; ed and trans Deems
Taylor Ger Eng (When sweetly blossom the roses) JF
4881; Ger Eng (Behold! The roses are blooming) Kal-

mus; Eng only (The red, red roses are blooming) pf
missing, in UPC 73 (Op. 44, 2, 7, 9)

no 8 Die Berge sind spitz   T: Paul Heyse 0:35 M-D;   in
P 3669b (Op. 44, 7–12);   ed and trans Deems Taylor Ger
Eng (The mountains are cold) JF 4880;   Ger Eng (The
mountains are steep) Kalmus

no 9 Am Windbach die Weiden   T: Paul Heyse 0:30
M-D;   in P 3669b (Op. 44, 7–12);   Ger Eng (The trees
by the river) Kalmus;   Eng only (The meadow at Wild-
bach) pf missing, in UPC 73 (Op. 44, 2, 7, 9)

no 10 Und gehst du über den Kirchhof   T: Paul Heyse
1:10 D;   in P 3669b (Op. 44, 7–12);   Ger Eng (O
shouldst thou pass) Kalmus

no 11 Die Braut (The bride)—Eine blaue Schürze hast du
mir gegeben   T: Wilhelm Müller 0:40x4 M-D;   in P
3669b (Op. 44, 7–12);   Ger Eng (See the blue-hued rib-
bon) Kalmus

no 12 Märznacht (A March night)—Horch! wie brauset der
Sturm   T: Uhland 1:00 D;   in P 3669b (Op. 44, 7–12);
Ger Eng (Hark! how roareth the storm) Kalmus;   Eng
only (Hark, the March wind is roaring), in UPC 66 (see
Brahms, Op. 113)

Op. 52 Liebeslieder (Love songs), in BrW XX, p 61–106 pf four
hands

no 4 Wie des Abends schöne Röte   T: Georg Friedrich
Daumer   SA 0:30x2 E-M;   ed HC-L trans Macfarren
Ger Eng (Like the sunsets crimson splendor), in Three
love songs (Op. 52, 4, 13;   Op. 65, 13) ES 1055;   Eng
only (Would that I were fair as sunset) pf missing in
Love songs (Op. 52) UPC 111

no 13 Vögelein durch-rauscht die Luft   T: Georg Friedrich Daumer   SA 0:25x2 M;   ed HC-L trans Macfarren Ger Eng (Bird in air will stray afar), in Three love
songs (Op. 52, 4, 13;   Op. 65, 13) ES 1055;   Eng only
(Thru the sky the swallow darts) pf missing, in Love songs
(Op. 52) UPC 111

Op. 65 Liebeslieder (Love songs), in BrW XX, p 107–146 pf four
hands

no. 13 Nein, Geliebter, setze dich   T: Georg Friedrich Daumer   SA 1:10x2 M;   ed HC-L trans Macfarren Ger Eng (Seat thyself, my dearest heart), in Three love songs (Op. 52, 4, 13;   Op. 65, 13) ES 1055;   Eng only (Nay, my dear, sit not so near) pf missing, in Love songs (Op. 65) UPC 112

Op. 66 Fünf Duette für Sopran und Alt (Five duets for soprano and alto), in BrW XXII, p 59–78 pf

no 1 Klänge (True lover's heart)—Aus der Erde quellen Blumen (From the kindly earth)   T: Klaus Groth SA 1:15 M;   trans Macfarren, ES 1530

no 5 Hüt du dich (Beware)—Ich weiss ein Mäd'lein hübsch und fein (I know a maiden fair to see)   T: fr Knaben Wunderhorn   SA 0:30x4 M;   trans and altered by Longfellow, ES 1531

Op. 113 Kanons (Canons), in BrW XXI, p 179–192 unac;   Ger only P 2648;   Ger Eng, Fourteen canons UPC 66 (also includes Op. 44, 12)

no 1 Göttlicher Morpheus (Heaven-born Morpheus)   T: Goethe   4 eq 1:30 E-M

no 2 Grausam erweiset sich Amor an mir (Cruel, ah cruel has love been to me)   T: Goethe   3 eq 1:40 E-M (not the same as Grausam erweiset, see below)

no 3 Sitzt a schöns Vögerl auf'm Dannabaum (What bird is that in the pinetree there)   T: Folksong   4 eq 0:30 E-M

no 4 Schlaf', Kindlein, schlaf'! (Sleep, baby, sleep)   T: Folksong   3 eq 2:00 M (see also Op. 113, no 4 below)

no 5 Wille wille will, der Mann ist kommen (Willie wille will, the man is coming)   T: Folksong   4 eq 0:30x3 E-M

no 6 So lange Schönheit wird bestehn (So long as beauty shall enthral)   T: Hoffman von Fallersleben   SSAA 1:15 E-M

no 7 Wenn die Klänge nah'n und fliehen (Sounds of music sweetly swelling)   T: Eichendorff   3 eq 1:40 E-M

no 8 Ein Gems auf dem Stein (A ram on the height)   T: Eichendorff   SSAA 1:00 E-M no 9 An's Auge des Liebsten (The eyes of the lovers)   T: Rückert   SSAA 0:35 E-M

no 10 Leise Töne der Brust (Softly plucking the chords) T: Rückert   4 eq 1:20 M

no 11 Ich weiss nicht (I wonder why)   T: Rückert   4 eq 1:10 E-M

no 12 Wenn Kummer hätte zu tödten (If grief were able to kill me)   T: Rückert   3 eq 2:00 M

no 13 Einförmig ist der Liebe Gram (Monotonous love's sad refrain)   T: Rückert 4:20 M

Op. 113, no 4 (Sleep, baby, sleep) Schlaf, Kindlein, schlaf [canon] 3 eq unac 2:00 M;   ed Martin, trans Elkin, Eng only, Elkin 2184 (American agent, Galaxy);   see also Op. 113, above

[Works without opus numbers]

Dein Herzlein mild (Thou gentle heart) [As later arr for SATB by Brahms, this became Op. 62, no 4, in BrW XXI, p 99] T: Paul Heyse   SSAA unac 1:00 E-M;   Eng only UPC 24

Der Englische Gruss (The angels' greeting)—Gegrüsset Maria SSAA unac 0:30x4 0:30 E-M;   Ger (included but not underlayed) Eng (All hail to Thee Mary), in Six Marienlieder UPC 75;   Ger Eng (We hail Thee, O Mary) music slightly altered ESV 887

Es geht ein Wehen (A sigh goes floating) [As later arr for SATTB by Brahms this became Op. 62, no 6, in BrW XXI, p 102] T: Paul Heyse   SSAA unac;   UPC 22

Grausam erweiset sich Amor an mir (Cruel, ah cruel hath love been to me) [canon], in BrW XXI, p 190   T: Goethe SSAA unac 1:00 E-M (not the same as Op. 113, no 2); w/Töne, in UPC 26

In stiller Nacht, see Todtenklang

Der Jäger (The hunter)—Es wollt gut Jäger jagen   SSAA unac 0:15x2 0:45 0:15 E-M;   Ger (included but not underlaid) Eng (A hunter went a-hunting), in Six Marienlieder UPC 75;   Ger Eng (A hunter went a-hunting) music slightly altered ESV 886

Magdalena (Mary Magdalene)—An dem österlichen Tag SSAA unac 0:20x3 M;   Ger (included but not underlaid)

Eng (Early on that Easter morn), in Six Marienlieder UPC
75; Ger Eng (Easter in the early morn) ESV 885
Marias Kirchgang (Mary and the boatman)—Maria wollt zur
Kirche gehn   SSAA unac 0:20x5 0:30 E-M;   Ger (in-
cluded but not underlaid) Eng (When Mary once to
church would go), in Six Marienlieder UPC 75;   Ger Eng
(When Mary to the church would go) music slightly altered
ESV 894
Marias Lob (Praise of Mary)—Maria, wahre Himmelsfreud
0:35x5 E;   Ger (included but not underlaid) Eng (Oh
Mary, joy of Heaven bright), in Six Marienlieder UPC 75;
Ger Eng (O Mary, joy of Heaven bright) ESV 896
Ruf zu Maria (Prayer to Mary)—Dich, Mutter Gottes, ruf'
wir an   SSAA unac 0:40x2 0:40 E-M;   Ger (included
but not underlaid) Eng (Oh Mother of God we cry to
Thee), in Six Marienlieder UPC 75;   Ger Eng (O Mother
of God we cry to Thee) music slightly altered ESV 895
Seven folk songs arr. by Brahms, 1859 [these compositions,
being settings of folk songs, do not properly belong in this
list, but are given here on account of their special interest]
unac E-M;   Ger (included but not underlaid) Eng, UPC
74

1. Altes Lied (Old song) [as arr by Brahms for solo voice,
   in BrW XXVI, p 138]—So will ich frisch und fröhlich
   seyn (In happy hope my heart today with cheer and
   joy is ringing)   SSAA 0:40

2. Der todte Gast (The dead youth) [as arr by Brahms
   for SATB, in BrW XXI, p 138, for solo voice in BrW
   XXVI, p 196]—Es pochet ein Knabe sachte (A lover
   is gently tapping on his sweetheart's window pane)
   SSA 0:25x5

3. Ich hab' die Nacht geträumet (At night when I was
   dreaming)   SSA 0:15x4

4. Altes Liebeslied (Old love song)—Mein Herzlein thut
   mir gar zu weh! (My soul is filled with fear and woe)
   SSAA 0:30x2

5. Es waren zwei Königskinder (The princess was watching the water)   SSA 0:15x5

6. Spannung (Lovers' quarrel)—Guten Abend, mein tausiger Schatz (God bless you, this ev'ning)   SSAA 0:20x6

7. Mit Lust thät ich ausreiten (The hunter)—(While I was gaily riding) [as arr by Brahms for SATB, in BrW XXI, p 129, for solo voice, in BrW XXVI, p 192] SSA 0:30x4

Six Marienlieder for SSAA [1859] [as later arr for SATB by Brahms these became Op. 22, in BrW XXI, p 1] (see individual titles for complete information);   UPC 75
Der Englische Gruss / Marias Kirchgang / Der Jäger / Ruf zu Maria / Magdelena / Marias Lob.

Suabian folk song, see Todtenklang

Todtenklang [also known as Suabian folk song]—In stiller Nacht [as arr by Brahms for SATB, in BrW XXI, p 136, for solo song, in BrW XXVI, p 183] T: Robert Herrick SSAA unac 1:10 M;   Ger Eng (In dead of night) UPC 23; ed KKD Eng only (Charm me asleep) music slightly altered 1:10x2, ES 1026

Töne lindernder Klang (Music, however soft) [canon] [as arr for SATB by Brahms, in BrW XXI, p 156]   SSAA unac 0:30x2 E-M;   w/Grausam, in UPC 26

Vineta [as later arr by Brahms for SAATBB this became Op. 42, no 2, in BrW XXI, p 82]—Aus des Meeres tiefen (Up from out the lowest depths) T: Wilhelm Müller SSAA unac 2:00 D;   UPC 21

BRASART, JOHANNES first half 15th C
O flos fragrans, in DTÖ VII, p 102   SSA or SII, etc. unac or I 3:15 M;   MCD 28. [In both MCD 28 and DTÖ VII, the third word, fragrans, is incorrectly given as flagrans.]

BREWER, THOMAS 1611–?
Turn Amarillis to thy swain   SSA unac 1:00 E;   Jos. Williams Ser. 17, no 21

BRIDGE, FRANK 1879–1941
Golden slumbers [1922] T: Thomas Dekker   SSA unac 3:00 E-M;   Au 15908

Hence care [1922]—Sing we and chant it   T: Anon. 1595
SSA unac 1:45 M;   Au 15907

BRITTEN, BENJAMIN 1913–
A ceremony of carols [Op. 28]   SSA, SS soli harp (pf) 18:45
(see below for more specific information);   BoHa (some titles,
as indicated below, available separately)

    1. Procession—Hodie Christus natus est   unison   harp
       (pf) ad lib. 1:05 E

    2. Wolcum yole!—Wolcum be thou hevenè king   SSA
       1:30 E-M;   BoHa 1755B

    3. There is no rose   SSA 2:00 E-M;   BoHa 1917

    4a. That yongë child   S solo 1:30 E-M

    4b. Balulalow—O my deare hart   SSA, S solo 1:15 E-M

    5. As dew in Aprille—I sing of a maiden   SSA 0:55 M

    6. This little Babe   T: Robert Southwell   SSA 1:15
       M-D;   BoHa 5138

    7. Interlude   harp (pf) only 3:00

    8. In freezing winter night—Behold, a silly babe   T:
       Robert Southwell   SSA, SA solo 3:10 M

    9. Spring carol—Pleasure it is to hear iwis   T: William
       Cornish   SS soli 1:10 E-M;   BoHa 1755A

    10. Deo gracias—Deo gracias! Adam lay ibounden   SSA
       2:50 D;   BoHa 5071

    11. Recessional (same as 1)

Missa brevis in D [Op. 63]—Kyrie eleison   SSA SSA soli org
Ky 1:40 Gl 2:40 Sa 1:10 Be 2:55 Ag 2:25 M;   score and voice
parts available separately, BoHa

The ride-by-nights, fr Three two-part songs—Upon their brooms
the witches stream   T: Walter de la Mare   SA pf 1:45
E-M;   OxOCS 168

The rainbow, fr Three two-part songs—I saw the lovely arch of
rainbow   T: Walter de la Mare   SA pf 2:00 E;   OxOCS
169

The ship of Rio, fr Three two-part songs—There was a ship of
Rio   T: Walter de la Mare   SA pf 2:15 E;   OxOCS 170

BROWN, HAROLD 1931–
Choral setting no 1—No worse there is none   T: Gerald
Manly Hopkins   SSAA unac 3:45 M;   Arrow

BRUCK (BROUCK), ARNOLD VON c. 1500–1554
Ave Maria   SSAA unac 1:00 M;   in JöG, p 95;   in Lei I, p 9
Da pacem, Domine   SSAA unac 1:30 M;   in Lei I, p 10;
   Lat Ger (Herr, schenk uns Frieden), in JöG, p 84
Pater noster   SSAA unac 2:00 M;   in Lei I, p 6

BRUDIEU, JOAN 1520?–1591
Ojos claros y serenos (Eyes so clear, so calm, so tender)
   SSAT(A) unac 2:40 E-M;   in Lehman Engel, Three centuries
   of choral music, V, p 83, Harold Flammer;   in Lehman
   Engel, Renaissance to Baroque . . . women's voices, p 65,
   Harold Flammer

BULLOCK, ERNEST 1890–
Echo—Come to me in the silence of the night   T: Christina
   Rossetti   SSA pf 3:00 E;   OxCS W6

BUSSER, HENRI-PAUL 1872–
Op. 88 La belle au bois dormant—C'est le château d'autrefois
   T: Gabriel Vicaire   SSAA, SA small chorus, S solo pf
   17:00 M;   voice parts published separately, Durand
Op. 104, no 1 J'ai mis mon coeur à la fenêtre   T: Gabriel
   Vicaire   SSA pf 2:20 M;   voice parts published separately,
   Durand

BYRD, WILLIAM 1542 or 1543–1623?
Benedictus—Blessed is he that cometh   SSA unac 1:00 E;
   w/Arne: Help, in SB Church choir lib 28
An earthly tree, a heavenly fruit, in EMS XV, p 145   SS string
   acc Eng 1:20 E
Hey ho, to the greenwood [canon]   3 eq unac 0:45 E;   w/Byrd:
   Non, Webbe: Would, in N SS 1895
In crystal towers   T: Geoffrey Whitney   SSA unac 2:25
   2:25x2 M;   in Da, p 56
Non nobis [canon] [misattributed, see Scholes, Oxford Com-
   panion]   T: Ps CXV   3 eq 1:20 E;   Cu 80598;   Lat Eng
   (Not unto us, O Lord), in RWOM, ESV 869;   w/Byrd: Hey
   ho, Webbe: Would you, in N SS 1895

Rejoice, rejoice with heart and voice, in EMS XV, p 141   T: Francis Kinwelmersch, 1576   SSAA unac 0:45 D;   SB M 15/24;   ESV 855

Short communion service—Lord have mercy   SSA unac Eng only Ky 0:20x3 Sa 1:00 Be 1:00 Ag 2:00 M;   SB 1970

Sing ye to our Lord, in EMS XVI, p 24   T: Ps CXLIX: 1-2 SSA unac 2:00 M-D;   SB M 16/6

BYTTERING, C. 15th C
Nesciens Mater (Knowing no man)   SAA(T) unac 1:30 M; SB Fayrfax 15

CALDARA, ANTONIO 1670–1736
Crucifixus   SSA unac 0:40 E;   in JöG, p 23

CALVISIUS, SETHUS 1556–1615
Ein feste Burg   T: Ps XLVI   SSA unac 0:30x2 0:30 M;   in GM, p 168

CAMPIAN, THOMAS 1567–1620
If love love truth   T: Campian?   SSA unac 0:15x2 0:20 E; ed Whittaker w/Gibbons, Silver swan (arr), in OxJP XXVI–XXVII

CAPLET, ANDRÉ 1878–1925
Inscriptions Champêtres   T: Rémy de Gourmont   SSA or SSA, SSA soli unac;   two editions, SSA and SSA, SSA soli, Durand

Messe a trois voix   SSA unac (orch ad lib.) Ky 3:20 Gl 7:00 Sa 1:50 Ag 2:00 O salutaris 2:10 M;   voice parts available separately, Durand

La miroir de Jésus   T: Henri Ghéon   SSA, SSA soli string orch harp Miroir de joie 15:30 . . . de peine 12:00 . . . de gloire 15:00 M;   voice parts available separately, Durand

CARTER, ELLIOTT 1908–
The harmony of morning   T: Mark van Doren   SSAA orch (pf) 8:30 M-D;   AM

CASCIOLINI, CLAUDIO c. 1670–?
Missa sine nomine   SSA unac Ky 0:15 Gl 1:40 Sa 0:20 Be
0:35 Ag 0:50 E;   Bank
Panis angelicus   SSA unac 1:30 E;   Z, no 6

CASTELNUOVO-TEDESCO, MARIO 1895–
Maria, stella maris (Mary, star of the sea)—Funde preces in
Coelis (Pour forth prayers in Heaven), fr Savonarola   T:
Girolamo Savonarola, trans Lois Neupert   SSA pf 2:00
E-M;   Galaxy

CEREROLS, JOAN ?–1676
Señor mio Jesu Christo   SSAA (one note, low C, may be
transposed) Bc 3:00 M;   in HAM II, p 90

CERTON, PIERRE c. 1510–1572
Benedictus, fr Missa Regnum mundi   SAT(A) unac 1:20 M;
in Lehman Engel, Three centuries of choral music, I, p 78,
Harold Flammer;   in Lehman Engel, Renaissance to Baroque
. . . women's voices, p 7, Harold Flammer
Je ne fus jamais si aise (Lasst uns tanzen)   SSA unac 1:00x2
E-M;   in Eur, p 30
Je n'ose être content (I cannot be content)   SA unac 1:15 E-M;
ed David w/Jocotin: Je suis, Sermisy: Auprès, Certon: Je
suis, in MP 34
Je suis tant bien (Such good I owe)   SA unac 1:45 E-M;   ed
David w/Certon: Je n'ose, Jocotin: Je suis, Sermisy:
Auprès, in MP 34

CHABRIER, EMMANUEL 1841–1894
A la musique—Musique adorable   T: Edmond Rostand
SSAA, S solo orch (pf) 5:00 M-D;   Enoch
La sulamite—Ô Sulamite! ô ma soeur!   T: Jean Richepin
SSAA, Mezzo S solo orch (pf) 16:00 D;   Enoch

CHADWICK, GEORGE WHITFIELD 1854–1931
Parvum quando cerno Deum (When I view the mother holding),
fr Noel   SSAA pf 3:15 E-M;   GrayCMR 239

CHANDLER, MARY 1911–
Hymn on the morning of Christ's nativity—It was the winter
wild   T: John Milton   SSA pf or harp 18:00 E;   N

CHARPENTIER, MARC ANTOINE 1634–1704
Ave Regina coelorum   SSA org 2:30 M;   acc missing,
Musique sacrée (obtain through WLSM)
Regina caeli   2 eq pf 2:45 E;   w/Sub tuum praesidium (uni-
son), in MR 2319

CHERUBINI, LUIGI 1760–1842
Ahi, ch'è il suon (Ach, was will das Bächlein sagen)   SS pf
(harp); in Duette, P 2108
Dite almeno (Zweige, werd ich)   SS pf (harp);   in Duette,
P 2108
Duette für zwei Soprane mit Begleitung des Pianoforte oder der
Harfe (see individual titles for complete information);   P
2108
    Ahi, ch'è il suon / Dite almeno / La mia Fille / Solitario
    bosco ombroso.
(Like as a father) Perfida clori [canon]   T: Ps CIII: 13
three eq pf 1:40 E;   Eng only, Summy-Brichard 5297
La mia Fille (Die Geliebte meines Lebens)   SS pf (harp);   in
Duette, P 2108
Solitario bosco ombroso (Waldesschatten breitet Kühle)   SS
pf (harp);   in Duette, P 2108

CHESNOKOFF (TSCHESNOKOFF), P. 1877–
(Praise ye the name of the Lord)   T: adapted Ivan Gorokhoff
SSAA unac 2:00 E-M;   GrayCMR 1151

CHIRBURY, ROBERT 15th C
Agnus Dei   SSA unac 1:00x2 0:15 M;   w/Sanctus, in SB
Fayrfax 11
Sanctus   SSA unac 1:55 M;   w/Agnus Dei, in SB Fayrfax 11

CICONIA, JOHANNES flourished c. 1400
Et in terra pax, in DTÖ XXXI, p 1   SSA unac 2:00 E-M;
in GM, p 22

CLARKE, HENRY LELAND

Et in terra pax   SSA (SII) unac 0:10 0:30x2 0:20 E-M;   in
HAM I, p 59

CLARKE, HENRY LELAND 1907–
Love-in-the-world—It looks on tempests   T: Genevieve Taggard   SSA, S(T) solo pf 3:15 E-M;   Mercury MC 348

CLAUDE LE JEUNE, see LE JEUNE, CLAUDE

CLEMENS NON PAPA, JACOBUS c. 1510–1555/1556
Mijn hartelijk lief (Mein schönes Lieb)   SSA unac 0:30x2 E;
in Eur, p 61
(Der Winter ist ein unwert Gast)   SSA unac 0:25x3 E;   in
JöW, p 60

CONSTANTINI, see COSTANTINI

COOPER, DR. ROBERT 15th–16th C
Gloria in excelsis   SSAA unac;   Ch

COPLAND, AARON 1900–
The house on the hill—They are all gone away   T: Edward
Arlington Robinson   SSAA unac 4:10 M;   ES 231
An immorality—Sing we for love and idleness   T: Ezra Pound
SSA, S solo pf 2:20 M;   ES 444
What do we plant?   T: Henry Abbey   SA pf 2:10 M;
BoHa 1639

CORFE, JOSEPH 1740–1820
I will magnify thee, O Lord   T: Ps XXX   two eq pf 1:30 E;
N Chorister 112

COSTANTINI (CONSTANTINI), ALESSANDRO c. 1643–?
Confitemini Domini   T: Ps CVI   SSA unac 1:15 E-M;   in
Tov, p 24

COUPERIN, FRANÇOIS 1663–1733
Troisième leçon de Ténèbres (Lamentations of Jeremiah), in
Oeuvres complètes de . . . [Complete works] XXI, p 225—
Jod. Manum suam misit hostis   T: Jeremiah I: 10–14
SS, SS soli Bc, strings ad lib. 9:30 M-D;   MCD 14

COWELL, HENRY 1897–
American muse   T: Stephen Vincent Benét   SA pf 2:00
1:20 2:00 E;   Mercury MP 57
1. American muse—American muse, whose strong and di-
verse heart
2. Swift runner—Swift runner, never captured or subdued
3. Immensity of wheel—And now to see you is more difficult yet
The lily's lament—The day was still and golden blurred   T:
Elizabeth Alen Lomax   SSAdiv pf 3:45 M;   AJ 5
Spring at summer's end—Into these hollows   T: Dora Hage-
meyer   SSA unac 4:00 M;   Peer WO 509
Supplication—God, enter my soul   Unison, 2 trumpets, 2 trombones, org, timpani B, C, F ad lib.   3:30 E;   score and I
parts, P 6322;   chorus score, P 6322a

CRANMER, PHILIP 20th C
Jesu dulcis memoria   T: 12th C   4 eq unac 2:15 M;   N Trios
633

CRAPPIUS, ANDREAS 1542–1623
(Holy is God, the Lord of Sabaoth) Jesaia, dem Propheten   T:
Martin Luther, 1526   SSA unac 1:05 E-M;   Eng only,
trans Parke S. Barnard, Con 98–1408
(Lord Jesus Christ, true man and God) Wir danken dir   T:
Paul Eber, 1511–1559   SSA unac 1:00 E-M;   Eng only,
trans Parke S. Barnard, Con 98–1406
(O Father full of mercy)   SSA unac 1:05 E-M;   Eng only,
trans Parke S. Barnard, Con 98–1407

CROCE, GIOVANNI c. 1560–1609
Ego sum pauper (When I was poor) T: Ps LIX: 29–30
SSAA unac 1:45 E-M;   ed and trans Williams, ES St. Dunstan
1282
Et resurrexit, fr Missa tertii toni   SSA 0:40 E-M;   in Tov,
p 19

CRUFT, ADRIAN 1921–
Farewell, ungrateful traitor [Op. 17, no 3]   T: John Dryden,

CSONKA, PAUL

1631–1700   SSA, S solo unac 1:00 M;   Joseph Williams
Ser. 17, no 30

CSONKA, PAUL 1905–

Concierto de Navidad (Christmas concert)—Cantad y bailad
(Come lad and be glad) T: trans C. M. Write   SSAA
harp 12:00 M; Pan American Union, Peer

DA NOLA, GIOVAN DOMENICO 1510?–1592

(Are all the ladies deaf) Chi la gagliarda T: Anon., trans
R. Maren   SSA unac 0:50x4 E; ed Zipper Eng only, AJ
36

DANIELS, MABEL 1879–

Carol of a rose—All of a rose T: Flemish 15th C   SSA,
SSA small chorus unac 0:35 1:05x2 0:40 E; GS 10632

DANYEL, JOHN c. 1565–1630

Now the earth, the skies, the air, in EFL Danyel, p 54   SS lute
(pf) 2:20 E; SB LU 34

DEBUSSY, CLAUDE 1862–1918

La demoiselle élue (The blessed damozel) T: Gabriel Rossetti   SSAA, MS solo orch (pf) 18:45 E-M (chorus) D (solo);
Eng only adapted Frank Damrosch, GS
Noël des enfants qui n'ont plus de maison (Christmas carol for
homeless children)—Nous n'avons plus de maison (We have
no more house nor home) T: Debussy, trans Swayne Saint
René Taillandier   SA pf 2:45 E-M; accompaniment missing, Durand

DECIUS, NIKOLAUS c. 1485–after 1546

(All glory be to God on high) Allein Gott in der Höh' sei Ehr'
T: Decius   SSA unac 0:45 E-M; Eng only, Con 98–1253

DEDEKIND, HENNING ?–1628

Trink ich Wein, so verderb ich   SSA unac 0:30x4 M; in
JöW, p 120
Wer will mir helfen klagen?   SSA unac 1:10 M; in JöW,
P 97

DELIUS, FREDERICK 1862–1934
The streamlet's slumber song—While beneath a cloudless sky
SS pf 1:00 E;   OxCS 115

DELLO JOIO, NORMAN 1913–
Adieu, Mignonne, when you are gone   T: Owen Meredith,
Earl of Lytton   SSA pf 3:45 M-D;   CF CM 6784

DERING, RICHARD 1575–1630
Above Him stood the seraphim   SS pf 3:00 E;   ed Roper,
Ox 44.709
Gloria Patri   SSA unac 1:20 M;   ed Whittaker, OxJP V
Hence vain affections   SSA unac 1:30x2 E-M;   ed Whittaker,
OxJP I
Tell me, fair but unkind   SSA unac 1:00 0:55x2;   ed Whit-
taker, OxJP III
When sad grief   SSA unac 0:30x2 0:25x2 E-M;   ed Whit-
taker, OxJP IV

DESPRÉS, JOSQUIN c. 1445–1521
Agnus Dei, fr Missa de Beata Virgine   SA unac 1:10 D;
w/Pleni, in MCD 25
Ave vera virginitas   SSAA unac 1:00 E-M;   Z, no 10
Ave verum corpus   T: attributed Pope Innocent VI   SSA
unac 1:15 1:30 0:50 D;   Lat Eng (Bread of heaven) ESV 2500;
1:15 1:30 in Lehman Engel, Renaissance to Baroque . . .
women's voices, p 4, Harold Flammer
Pleni sunt coeli, fr Missa Pange lingua   SS unac 1:55 D;
w/Agnus, in MCD 25;   ExRP 2949;   in Das Chorwerk I,
p 20, Möseler

DIAMOND, DAVID 1915–
All in green went my love riding [1947]   T: E. E. Cummings
SSA unac 2:00 M;   Southern
The glory is fallen out of the sky [1940]   T: E. E. Cummings
SSA unac 2:00 M-D;   Southern
Young Joseph [1944]—The stillness lay upon the vineyards   T:
Thomas Mann   SSA string orch (pf) 6:00 M-D;   Mercury
MP 105

33

DIETRICH, FRITZ 1905–1945?

Dreikönigskantata (The three kings, a cantata for Epiphany)
—Nun macht euch auf (Arise, ye kings, do not delay) T: fr
Knaben Wunderhorn   SA, various simple soli 2 flutes (recorders) 2 vio bass I 11:30 E-M; I, voice pts and score available, Ger only, Bä 1036;   Eng only, trans Theo. Klammer,
flute pts Con 97–6367, vio I and II Con 97–6374, bass I Con
97–6375, score Con 97–6362

Kleine Weihnachtskantata nach dem Evangelisten Lukas (A
little Christmas cantata according to the Evangelist St. Luke)
—Gelobet seist Du (All praise to Thee)   SA, S(T) soli 2
flutes (recorders) 2 vio, bass I 17:20 E; I, voice pts, and score
available, Ger only, Bä 955;   Eng only, flute pts Con 97–6285,
vio I and II Con 97–6284, bass I Con 97–6286, score Con
97–6277

DIETRICH, SIXTUS c. 1490–1548

Gib uns heut unser täglich Brot   SSA unac 1:20 E-M; in
JöG, p 72

DISTLER, HUGO 1908–1942

Ach Gott, vom Himmel sieh darein   SSA unac 1:00x2 1:00
E-M; in Jahrkreis, Bä 676

Das Amen—Amen   SSA unac 0:30 0:30 0:30 M; in Jahrkreis,
Bä 676

Bei stiller Nacht   SSA unac 0:40x5 E-M; in Jahrkreis, Bä
676

Bescher uns, Herr, das täglich Brot   SSA unac 0:45x6 M; in
Jahrkreis, Bä 676

Christ fuhr gen Himmel 2:00 M-D; in Jahrkreis, Bä 676

Dreimaliges Kyrie Nürnberg 1525 [1st setting]—Herre, erbarm
dich unser! 2 eq unac 1:00 M-D; w/Dreimaliges Kyrie
Strassburg, Dreimaliges Kyrie Nürnberg [2d setting], in Bä
1043

Dreimaliges Kyrie Nürnberg 1525 [2d setting]—Herre, erbarm
dich unser! 3 eq unac 0:30 M-D; w/Dreimaliges Kyrie
Strassburg, Dreimaliges Kyrie Nürnberg [1st setting] in Bä
1043

Dreimaliges Kyrie Strassburg 1525—Kyrie eleison 3 eq unac

Lat and Ger 1:15 M-D; w/Dreimaliges Kyrie Nürnberg [two settings], in Bä 1043

Ehre sei Gott in der Höhe   SSA unac 1:15 M-D; in Jahrkreis, Bä 676

Er ist's—Frühling lässt sein blaues Band   T: Mörike   SA unac 1:00 M-D; w/Jägerlied, Verborgenheit, in Bä 1540; in Mörike, Bä 1516; in Mörike, Bä 1517

Erschienen ist der herrlich' Tag   SSA unac w/1 ritornello 0:30x5, ritornello 0:30 E-M; in Jahrkreis, Bä 676

Erstes Liebeslied eines Mädchens—Was im Netze?   T: Mörike SSAA unac 1:30 M; Bä 1548; in Mörike, Bä 1516; in Mörike, Bä 1517

Es ist das Heil uns kommen her   SSA unac 2:30 M-D; in Jahrkreis, Bä 676

Es kommt ein Schiff, geladen   SSA unac 0:20x6 M; in Jahrkreis, Bä 676

Der Gärtner [2d setting]—Auf ihrem Leibrösslein   T: Mörike SSAA unac 0:25x4 M; w/Gebet [1st setting] in Bä 1544; in Mörike, Bä 1516; in Mörike, Bä 1517

Gebet [1st setting]—Herr, schikke, was du willt   T: Mörike SA unac 0:30x2 0:15 M; w/Der Gärtner in Bä 1544; in Mörike, Bä 1516; in Mörike, Bä 1517

Gebet [2d setting]—Herr, schikke, was du willt   T: Mörike SSA unac 0:30x2 0:30 M; Bä 1545; in Mörike, Bä 1516; in Mörike, Bä 1517

Gott ist unsre Zuversicht   SSA unac 1:30 M; in Jahrkreis, Bä 676

Die helle Sonn' leucht't jetzt herfür   0:25x2 0:25 E-M; in Jahrkreis, Bä 676

Herr, schicke, was du willt   T: Mörike   SSA unac 1:30 M; in Jahrkreis, Bä 676

Hinunter ist der Sonne Schein   SSA unac 0:50x2 0:50 M; in Jahrkreis, Bä 676

In Gottes Names fahren wir   SSA unac 0:40x3 E-M; in Jahrkreis, Bä 676

Jägerlied [1st setting]—Zierlich ist des Vogels Tritt   T: Mörike   SSA unac 0:45x2 M; w/Er ist's, Verborgenheit, in Bä 1540; in Mörike, Bä 1516; in Mörike, Bä 1517

Der Jahrkreis [Op. 5] (see individual titles for complete information); Bä 676

O Heiland, reiss die Himmel auf / Es kommt ein Schiff, geladen / Macht hoch die Tür / Ehre sei Gott in der Höhe / Lobt Gott, ihr Christen, allzugleich / Ein Lämmlein geht und trägt die Schuld / Bei stiller Nacht / Jesu, deine Passion / O Mensch, bewein dein' Sünde gross / Erschienen ist der herrlich' Tag / Mit Freuden zart / Christ fuhr gen Himmel / Nun bitten wir den heiligen Geist / Ein neu Gebot gebe ich euch / Wir glauben an Gott, den Vater / Ach Gott, vom Himmel sieh darein / Wach auf, mein's Herzens Schöne / Gott ist unser Zuversicht / Es ist das Heile uns kommen her / Wohlauf mit mir auf diesen Plan / Der Mensch, vom Weibe geboren, lebt kurze Zeit / Wach auf, wach auf, du deutsches Land / In Gottes Namen fahren wir / Wo Gott zu Haus nit gibt sein' Gunst / Die helle Sonn' leucht't jetzt herfür / Hinunter ist der Sonne Schein / Bescher uns, Herr, das täglich Brot / Vaterunser / Herr, schicke, was du willt / Das Amen / (and 22 titles not suitable for performance by women's voices).

Jesu, deine Passion   SSA unac 1:00x6 E-M; in Jahrkreis, Bä 676

Ein Lämmlein geht und trägt die Schuld   SSA unac 1:30x9 M; in Jahrkreis, Bä 676

Lied vom Winde—Sausewind, Brausewind! T: Mörike SSA unac 1:30 M-D; Bä 1547; in Mörike, Bä 1516; in Mörike, Bä 1517

Lobt Gott, ihr Christen, allzugleich   SSA unac 1:00x5 M; in Jahrkreis, Bä 676

Macht hoch die Tür   SSA unac 0:45x5 M; in Jahrkreis, Bä 676

Mausfallensprüchlein—Kleine Gäste, kleines Haus T: Mörike SA unac 1:20 M-D; Bä 1542; in Mörike, Bä 1516; in Mörike, Bä 1517

Der Mensch, vom Weibe geboren, lebt kurze Zeit   SSA unac 2:00 M; in Jahrkreis, Bä 676

Mit Freuden Zart   SSA unac 1:00x4 1:00 M; in Jahrkreis, Bä 676

Mörike-Chorliederbuch [Op. 19] (see individual titles for complete information); complete edition with sections for mixed, women's, and men's voices, Bä 1516; second section only, for women's voices, Bä 1517; each title also published separately as indicated after individual titles
>Contents of all pieces for women's voices: Er ist's / Jägerlied [1st setting] / Verborgenheit [1st setting] / Die Tochter der Heide [2d setting] / Mausfallensprüchlein / Die Soldatenbraut / Gebet [1st setting] / Der Gärtner [2d setting] / Gebet [2d setting] / Das verlassene Mägdlein / Lied vom Winde / Erstes Liebeslied eines Mädchens.

Ein neu Gebot gebe ich euch SSA unac 1:30 M; in Jahrkreis, Bä 676

Nun bitten wir den heiligen Geist SSA unac w/I ritornello 0:45x4, ritornello 0:45 E-M; in Jahrkreis, Bä 676

O Heiland, reiss die Himmel auf SSA unac 0:20x6 M; in Jahrkreis, Bä 676

O Mensch, bewein dein' Sünde gross SSA unac 1:00x2 E-M; in Jahrkreis, Bä 676

Die Soldatenbraut—Ach, wenn's nur der König auch wüsst' T: Mörike SSA unac 1:10 0:40x3 M; Bä 1543; in Mörike, Bä 1516; in Mörike, Bä 1517

Die Tochter der Heide [2d setting]—Wasch, dich, mein Schwesterchen T: Mörike SSA unac 0:45x4 M; Bä 1541; in Mörike, Bä 1516; in Mörike, Bä 1517

Vater unser im Himmelreich SSA unac 1:00x5 1:00x4 E-M; in Jahrkreis, Bä 676

Verborgenheit [1st setting]—Lass, o Welt T: Mörike SA unac 0:25x4 M; w/Er ist's, Jägerlied, in Bä 1540; in Mörike, Bä 1516; in Mörike, Bä 1517

Das verlassene Mägdlein—Früh, wann die Hähne krähn T: Mörike SSAA unac 0:30x4 M; Bä 1546; in Mörike, Bä 1516; in Mörike, Bä 1517

Wach auf, mein's Herzens Schöne SSA unac 0:45x3 0:45 E-M; in Jahrkreis, Bä 676

Wach auf, wach auf, du deutsches Land SSA unac 0:20x2 0:40 E-M; in Jahrkreis, Bä 676

Wir glauben an Gott, den Vater   SSA unac 1:30 E-M;   in
Jahrkreis, Bä 676

Wo Gott zu Haus nit gibt sein Gunst   SSA unac 0:30x3 M;
in Jahrkreis, Bä 676

Wohlauf mit mir auf diesen Plan   SSA unac 0:40x3 0:40
E-M;   in Jahrkreis, Bä 676

DOHNÁNYI, ERNST VON 1877-1960

Stabat Mater [Op. 46]   SSASSA, SSA soli, orch (pf) 23:00 M;
Am A-219

DONOVAN, RICHARD 1891-

Chanson of the bells of Osenèy—The bells of Osenèy   T: Cale
Young Rice   SSAA pf 4:00 E;   Galaxy 549

Dawn, no 1 of Songs of nature—Soft putterings of rain on roof
T: Frances Fenton Park   SSA pf 1:45 M;   Am A-184

For a mocking voice—Who calls?   T: Eleanor Farjeon
SSAA unac 5:00 M;   Kalmus

For snow—Oh the falling snow   T: Eleanor Farjeon   SSAA
unac 2:20 E-M;   Kalmus

How should I love?—The maidens came when I was in my
mother's bower   SSAA pf 3:40 M-D;   MP 104

Songs of nature   T: Frances Fenton Park (see individual titles
for complete information);   each title published separately
1. Dawn / 2. Wind sings / 3. The yellow lilly / 4. Wind of
heaven

The wind blows north   T: Eleanor Farjeon   SSAA unac
3:00 M;   Kalmus

Wind of heaven, no 4 of Songs of nature—Oh wind of heav'n
T: Frances Fenton Park   SSA pf 2:45 M;   Am A-187

Wind sings, no 2 of Songs of nature—Within the corner of the
house   T: Frances Fenton Park   SSA div pf 0:45 M;
Am A-185

The yellow lilly, no 3 of Songs of nature—The yellow lily,
poised on slender stem   T: Frances Fenton Park   SSA
pf 2:00 E-M;   Am A-186

DOUGLAS, WINFRED 1867-

I sing of a maiden   T: 15th C   SSA unac 1:20 E;   Gray-
CMR 1245

DUCASSE, see ROGER-DUCASSE

DUCIS, BENEDICT c. 1480–1544
  Nun freut euch, lieben Christen gmein   SSAA unac 1:30 M;
    in JöG, p 2

DUFAY, GUILLAUME c. 1400–1474
  Flos florum   SAA unac 4:00 D; in Ste, p 14
  Gloria in excelsis deo "ad modum tubae" [canon], in DTÖ
    VII, p 145   SSAA unac 2:00 M; Bank [AA parts, to be
    sung "in the style of trombones," textless in original, missing
    in this edition]; w/words added to AA in Lehman Engel,
    Three centuries of choral music I, p 11, Harold Flammer
  Magnificat in the eighth mode—Magnificat anima mea Domi-
    num   T: Luke I: 46–55   SSA (SAI) 5:00 M-D; MCD 29
  Veni creator spiritus—Qui paraclitus diceris   SAA (SII) unac
    0:40 E-M; in MET, p 37

DUKE, JOHN 1899–
  O sing unto the Lord a new song   T: fr the Psalms   SSA
    org 7:10 M; GS 10650

DUKELSKY, VLADIMIR 1903–
  The shepherd's holiday—The month of May is now begun   T:
    Victorian street ballad   SSA unac 1:15 E-M; CF CM 5328

DUNSTABLE, JOHN c. 1370–1453
  Quam pulcra est, in MB VIII, p 112   T: Canticle of canticles
    SAA unac 1:55 M-D; in Ste, p 19; in Lehman Engel, Ren-
    aissance to Baroque . . . women's voices, p 35, Harold Flammer
  Veni sancte spiritus/Veni creator, in MB VIII, p 88   SSA,
    SSA soli, unison I 4:30 M-D; SB 5308-2

DUNSTAN, RALPH 1857–1933
  Missa in festis duplicibus   SSAA unac; Cu

DVOŘÁK, ANTONIN 1841–1904
  Op. 29, no 2 Das Vöglein (The birdling)—Fliege, Vöglein (Fly,
    bright birdling)   SA pf 3:25 E-M; ES 1532
  NOTE: All thirteen of the Moravian duets (sometimes designated
    Opus 29 and 32), formerly published by G. Schirmer, are now
    out of print. The unusually fine pieces, although perhaps

best performed by two solo voices, are of great worth to the women's chorus. All will be available in the complete works of Dvořák, Series VI, vol 3 (proposed). Unfortunately this edition will not be suitable for performance due to its size and cost.

EAST (ESTE), MICHAEL 1580–1648
How merrily we live, in EMS XXX, p 13   SSA unac 2:10 E-M;   Gray MS 672;   ed HC-L, ES 1062;   revised G. Holst, GS 5359
I did her woo, EMS XXXI, part 2, p 7   SSAA unac 0:30 0:30x2 E-M;   SB M 31/2
See Amaryllis shamed, in EMS XXX, p 6   SSA unac 0:20 0:25x2;   SB M 30/2
Thyrsis, sleepest thou, in EMS XXXI, part 2, p 1   SSAA unac 1:30 0:40x2 M;   SB M 31/1
Whenas I glance, in EMS XXXI, part 2, p 17   SSAA unac 1:45 M;   SB M 31/5
Why are our summer sports, in EMS XXXI, p 10   SSAA unac 0:45 0:30x2 M;   SB M 31/3
Why smilest thou?, in EMS XXX, p 9   SSA unac 1:15 E; SB M 30/3

ECCARD, JOHANN 1553–1611
Der Kuckuck auf dem Dache sass   SSAA unac 2:00 M;   in JöW, p 53
Der Tag der ist so freudenreich   SSAA unac 2:10 M;   in JöG, p 5
Unsre lieben Hühnerchen   SSA unac 1:15 M;   in JöW, p 131

ECCLES, JOHN 1668–1735
Hark! Harry (Horch, Heinrich) [canon]   3 eq unac 1:30 E-M; in GM, p 354

ELKUS, JONATHAN 1931–
Chantey—Fifteen men on the dead man's chest   3 eq unac 0:30 E;   in Four three-part, N SS 2041
Cheyenne Mountain—Purple shadows, eastward falling   3 eq unac 0:45 E;   in Four three-part, N SS 2041

Four three-part catches (see individual titles for complete information);   N SS 2041
    Huck Finn's song / Chantey / Cheyenne Mountain / To Californy-a!

Huck Finn's song—Smoking's a pleasure   3 eq unac 0:30 E; in Four three-part, N SS 2041

To Californy-a!—Come all you yankey farmers   3 eq unac 0:30 E;   in Four three-part, N SS 2041

ELSBETH, THOMAS ?–after 1624
Freunde, so lasst uns jetzung singen   SSA unac 0:15x2 E-M; in Eur, p 62;   same music as Harre des Herrn, in JöG, p 124

Harre des Herrn   SSA unac 0:15x2 E-M;   in JöG, p 124; same music as Freunde, so lasst uns jetzung singen, in Eur, p 62

Wollt ich nicht fröhlich singen   SSA unac 0:40x2 0:35 E-M; in JöG, p 65

ENGEL, LEHMAN A. 1910–
The blossom, fr Songs of innocence—Merry, merry sparrow!
T: William Blake   SSA unac 0:25 M;   w/The lamb, BoHa Arrow

Hist whist little ghost things, fr Chansons innocents   T: E. E. Cummings   SSA pf 0:45 M-D;   w/In just spring, Tumbling-hair, BoHa Arrow

In just spring when the world is mud, fr Chansons innocents
T: E. E. Cummings   SSA pf 1:10 M-D;   w/Hist whist, Tumbling-hair, BoHa Arrow

The lamb, fr Songs of innocence—Little lamb who made thee?
T: William Blake   SSA unac 1:25 M;   w/The blossom, BoHa Arrow

Tumbling-hair picker of buttercups, fr Chansons innocents   T: E. E. Cummings   SSA pf 1:10 M-D;   w/In just spring, Hist whist, BoHa Arrow

ERPF, HERMANN 1891–
Festliches Lied—Einmal nur in unserm Leben   T: Goethe
SSA unac 0:15x4 E;   in JöW, p 33

ESTE, see EAST

ETLER, ALVIN 1913–
Under stars—I lay on the grass unmindful   T: Etler   SSA
   unac 2:30 E-M;   AM A–341
Under the cottonwood tree—I lay under the cottonwood tree
   T: Etler   SA unac 1:40 E-M;   AM A–342

FAURÉ, GABRIEL 1845–1924
Agnus Dei   SSS org;   Heugel 23304
Ave verum (Jesus word, of God incarnate) [Op. 65, no 1]   SA
   org 2:10 E;   ESV 860;   Lat only w/Maria, Tantum ergo, and
   others not suitable for women's voices, in Musique Religieuse
   par . . . , Hamelle
Maria, Mater gratiae [Op. 47, no 2]   SA pf 2:00 E;   w/Ave
   verum, Tantum ergo, and others not suitable for women's
   voices, in Musique Religieuse par . . . , Hamelle
Messe Basse   SAdiv org Ky 1:15 Sa 1:30 Be 0:50 Ag 2:20 E-M;
   Heugel;   Mercury 275
Tantum ergo [Op. 65, no 2]   T: Thomas Aquinas, 1227–1274
   SSA, SSA soli org 2:10 E-M;   Lat Eng (Therefore we, before
   Him bending), ESV 861;   Lat only w/Maria, Ave verum, and
   others not suitable for women's voices, in Musique Religieuse
   par . . . , Hamelle;   Lat Eng (Such a single bright affection),
   Broude 149

FERRABOSCO, ALFONSO 1575–1628
In Thee, O Lord   T: Sir William Leighton   SSAA unac
   1:05x3 M;   in Da, p 84

FESTA, COSTANZO 1519–1545
Ave Regina coelorum   SSA unac 4:00 M;   Bank
Quam pulcra es   T: Canticle of canticles   SSA unac 1:30
   E-M;   Bank
Sancta Maria, succurre   SSA unac 2:40 E;   Bank

FINE, IRVING 1914–1962
Beautiful soup, no 3 of Three choruses from Alice in Wonder-
   land, 2d series—Beautiful soup, so rich and green   T: Lewis
   Carroll   SSA pf 1:40 M;   W 2-W 3495

Caroline Million, fr The choral New Yorker   T: Isabel Mac-
Meekin   SSAA, SA soli pf 4:10 M;   W 3-W 3267(11)
Father William, no 3 of Three choruses from Alice in Wonder-
land, 1st series—You are old, Father William   T: Lewis
Carroll   SSA pf (orch) 2:15 M;   W 2-W 3204
The knave's letter, no 1 of Three choruses from Alice in Wonder-
land, 2d series—They told me you had been to her   T: Lewis
Carroll   SSA pf 2:15 M;   W 2-W 3493
The lobster quadrille, no 1 of Three choruses from Alice in
Wonderland, 1st series—Will you walk a little faster   T:
Lewis Carroll   SSA pf (orch) 3:00 E;   W 2-W 3205
Lullaby of the duchess, no 2 of Three choruses from Alice in
Wonderland, 1st series—Speak roughly   T: Lewis Carroll
SSA pf (orch) 2:00x2 E-M;   W 2-W 3206
Three choruses from Alice in Wonderland (see individual titles
for complete information)
      1st series: The lobster quadrille / Lullaby of the duchess /
      Father William / 2d series: The knave's letter / The white
      knight's song / Beautiful soup.
The white knight's song, no 2 of Three choruses from Alice in
Wonderland—I'll tell thee ev'rything that I can   T: Lewis
Carroll   SA, S solo pf 1:40x2 0:20 M;   W 1-W 3494

FIORAVANTI, VALENTINO 1769–1837
O vos omnes   SSAA unac 1:00 E;   Z, no 8

FORSBLAD, LELAND 1921–
Immortal Babe [canon]—Immortal Babe, who this dear day   T:
16th C   SSA unac 1:40 E;   Harold Flammer 89163

FRACKENPOHL, ARTHUR 1924–
A boy of Bagdad [canon]—There once was a boy of Bagdad
SA pf 1:50 E;   in Three limericks, AJ 90
A diner at Crewe [canon]—A diner while dining at Crewe
SA pf 0:50 E;   in Three limericks, AJ 90
A fellow of Perth [canon]—There was a young fellow of Perth
SA pf 0:50 E;   in Three limericks, AJ 90
Three limericks in canon form (see individual titles for com-
plete information);   AJ 90
      A diner at Crewe / A boy of Bagdad / A fellow of Perth.

FRANCK, CÉSAR 1822–1890

L'ange gardiene (The guardian angel)—Veillez sur moi (Watch over me)   SA pf 3:20 E; Fr only, in Six duos, Enoch 8206;   trans KKD, Eng only, ES 498

Aux petits enfants—Enfants d'un jour   T: Alphonse Daudet SA pf 1:45 E-M;   in Six duos, Enoch 8206

La chanson du Vannier—Brins d'osier   T: A. Theuriet   SA pf 4:00 E;   in Six duos, Enoch 8206

Les danses de Lormont—Poursuivant les nué   T: Desbordes Valmore   SA pf 4:15 E-M;   in Six duos, Enoch 8206

Premier sourire de Mai—Au premier sourire du soleil   T: Victor Wilder   SA pf 2:15 M;   Hamelle 3088

Six duos pour chant et piano (see individual titles for complete information);   Enoch 8206

L'ange gardien / Aux petits enfants / La Vierge à la crèche / Les danses de Lormont / Soleil / La chanson du Vannier.

Soleil—Incendiant les horizons   T: Guy Ropartz   SA pf 2:30 E;   in Six duos, Enoch 8206

La Vierge à la crèche—Dans ses langes blancs fraîchement cousus T: Alphonse Daudet   SA pf 2:45 E;   in Six duos, Enoch 8206;   Eng only (The Virgin by the manger—In a new white gown) trans Henry Chapman, GS 5520;   Fr Eng (The Virgin by the manger—Clothed in spotless white) trans E. A. Barrell, Presser 20751;   Fr Eng (At the cradle—In his swaddling clothes) trans KKD, ES 1533

FREED, ISADORE 1900–1960

In distress I called upon the Lord   T: fr Ps CXVIII   SSA, Baritone (mezzo S) solo pf (org) or orch 8:00 M;   score and parts on rental, vocal score no 310, Transcontinental Music Corp., 1674 Broadway, NYC

FRIDERICI, DANIEL 1580–1638

Mit Lust, will ich mein Zeit zubringen   SSA unac 0:35x2 E; in JöW, p 14

GABRIELI, ANDREA c. 1510–1586

Crucifixus, fr Missa Pater peccavi   SSA unac 1:40 M;   in Tov, p 17

(Love has become a stranger) Forestier inamorao T: Antonio
Molino   SSA unac 2:30 E-M; Eng only, trans R. Maren,
AJ 43

GÁL, HANS 1890–
Op. 5 Phantasien [1919] T: Rabindranath Tagore   SSAA,
A solo strings, clarinet, horn, harp (pf); piano score U 6361
1. Ich laufe wie ein Bisam 5:00 M
2. Ich pflückte deine Blume 4:00 E-M
3. Was flüsterst du so matt   SSAA div, no solo 7:30 M
Op. 14 Kinderverse T: Paula Dehmel   SSAA pf ad lib.;
Tischner und Jagenberg, Köln am Rhein
1. Eingang—Putzt die Fenster!   SSAA div 1:30 M
2. Geht leise 2:10 D
3. Kehrreim—Ich bau ein steinern Haus 0:10 0:15x2 E-M
4. Gutenachtliedchen—Leise, Peterle, leise 0:20x3 E-M
5. Hänsel und Gretel stehen zu zwein 0:30x2 0:15 M
6. Vom Monde—Wind, sause 2:20 E-M
7. Ausklang—Aus lichtem See   SSAA div 3:00 M
Op. 25 Herbstlieder   SSAA unac; Simrock 14832
1. Der Schnitter—Es ist ein Schnitter T: Folksong
2. Herbstgefühl—Fetter grune T: Goethe
3. Regenlied—So regnet es sich langsam ein T: C.
Flaischen
4. Weisheit des Hafis—Ob feinselige Winde T: Daumer
5. Erhebung—Die Blätter fallen T: Rilke
Op. 31 Drei Lieder T: Rilke   SSA pf; Simrock 1004
1. Advent—Es treibt der Wind 1:40 M
2. Adagio—Der Abend ist mein Buch 3:10 M
3. Sankt Nepomuk—Grosse Heilige und kleine feiert jeg-
liche Gemeine 1:40 M
Op. 47 Stille Lieder (Summer idylls) T: Caesar Flaischlen
SSAA unac; Eng only, Ger included but not underlaid,
UPC 146
1. Sonnentage (Days of sunshine)—Einzig schöne Tag (Days
of quiet gladness) 4:00 M
2. Ganz still einmal (Might I for once)—Ganz still einmal
(For once O might I) 4:00 M-D

3. Scherzando (Begone dull care)—Da bist auch du ja wieder (So there you are again) 1:30 M

4. Ende (Finis)—Verträumt und müde (Exhausted and fainting) 4:00 M-D

Op. 51a, no 1 True love—My true love hath my heart   T: Sir Philip Sidney, 1598   SSAA unac 2:15 M;   N Trios 592

Op. 75 Songs of youth (see individual titles for complete information)

Crabbed age and youth / Love is a sickness / Tell me where is fancy bred / Capriccio / Epilogue.

Capriccio, no 4 of cycle Songs of youth [Op. 75]—Love in my bosom like a bee   T: Thomas Lodge, 1556–1625   SSAA unac 3:30 M;   BoHa 18614

Crabbed age and youth, no 1 of cycle Songs of youth [Op. 75]   T: Anon., 1599   SSAA unac 2:30 M;   BoHa 18611

Epilogue, no 5 of cycle Songs of youth [Op. 75]—All my past life is mine no more   T: Earl of Rochester, 1647–1680 SSA unac 3:00 M;   BoHa 18615

Love is a sickness, no 2 of cycle Songs of youth [Op. 75]   T: Samuel Daniel, 1562–1619   SSAA unac 0:50x2 E-M; BoHa 18612

Tell me where is fancy bred, no 3 of cycle Songs of youth [Op. 75]   SSAA unac;   BoHa 18613

GALLUS, see HÁNDL, JACOB

GAMBLE, JOHN c. 1615–1687
Will Cloris cast her sunbright eye?   SSA unac 0:35x2 E; w/H. Lawes: Come, in Jos. Williams Series 17, no 19

GASPARINI, FRANCESCO 1665–1729
Mass in G   SSSAA, S solo Bc Ky 5:45 Gl 10:45 Cr 9:00 Sa 1:00 Ag 1:15 M;   Bc missing UPC (score w/Bc in New York Public Library)

GASTOLDI, GIOVANNI 1556–1622
In eurer Lieb ich   SSA unac 1:00x2 E-M;   in JöW, p 66
Mein Gedanken tun mich zwingen   SSA unac 0:30x2 E-M; in JöW, p 9

46

GÉDALGE, ANDRÉ 1856–1926
Été Indien—Les gais parfums   T: F. Herold   SA, A solo
pf 2:45 E-M;   pf missing, Legouix

GENZMER, HARALD 1909–
Alte Lieder in neuen Sätzen (see individual titles for complete
information);   Bä 3636
> Ich fahr dahin / All mein Gedanken / Alter Reigen um
> das erste Veilchen / So treiben wir den Winter aus / Grüss
> Gott, du schöner Maie / Der Gutzgauch auf dem Zaune
> sass / Maienzeit bannet Leid / Weiss mir ein Blümlein
> blaue / Es waren zwei Königskinder / Der grimmig Tod
> mit seinem Pfeil / Den Ackermann soll man loben.
Den Ackermann soll man loben   T: fr Lothringen   SA
unac 0:30x3 E-M;   in Alte, Bä 3636
All mein Gedanken   T: fr Locheimer Liederbuch, 1452
SSA unac 0:30x2 E;   in Alte, Bä 3636
Alter Reigen um das erste Veilchen—Der Maie bringt uns der
Blümlein   SSA unac 0:20x3 E;   in Alte, Bä 3636
Es waren zwei Königskinder   T: Umgebung von Bonn, 1819
SSA unac 0:15x16 E;   in Alte, Bä 3636
Der grimmig Tod mit seinem Pfeil   SSA unac 0:45x3 E-M;
in Alte, Bä 3636
Grüss Gott, du schöner Maie   T: Simrock, 1851   SSA unac
0:40x2 E;   in Alte, Bä 3636
Der Gutzgauch auf dem Zaune sass   SSA unac 0:30x3 E-M;
in Alte, Bä 3636
Ich fahr dahin   T: fr Locheimer Liederbuch, 1452   SSA
unac 0:40x2 E;   in Alte, Bä 3636
Maienzeit bannet Leid   T: after Max Pohl   SSA unac 0:40
E-M;   in Alte, Bä 3636
So treiben wir den Winter aus   SSAA unac 0:30x2 0:30 E;
in Alte, Bä 3636
Weiss mir ein Blümlein blaue   SSA unac 0:45x3 E-M;   in
Alte, Bä 3636

GERHARDT, CARL 1900–
Tischspruch [1930]—Erde, die uns dies gebracht   T: Morgenstern   SSAA unac 0:45 E-M;   in JöW, p 21

GÉRO, JEAN 16th C
Quand je bois du vin clairet (Wenn ich trinke gutten Wein)
SA unac 2:00 E;   in Eur, p 13

GESIUS, BARTHOLOMÄUS c. 1560–c. 1613
Der du bist drei in Einigkeit   SSA unac 0:30x2 E-M;   in
JöG, p 80
O Vater aller Frommen   SSA unac 0:25 E-M;   in JöG, p 75

GEVAERT, FRANÇOIS AUGUSTE 1828–1908
Grand Messe de Noël Puer natus est nobis   SSA org Ky Gl
Cr Sa Ag;   Lemoine 20337H
O filii et filiae (O sons and daughters)   T: Jean Tisserand
SSA unac 2:00 E-M;   trans J. M. Neale and EHG, ESV 868
Pater noster (The Lord's prayer)—Pater noster quies in coelis
(Our Father, who art in heaven)   SSA unac 2:45 E;   ed
Arthur S. Talmadge, ES 2502

GLASER, VICTORIA 1918–
An idle song   T: Anna B. True   SSA unac 1:20 M;   ES
2517

GODEBRYE, JACQUES, see JACOTIN

GOODMAN, ALFRED GRANT 20th C
Psalm XII—Save oh Lord for the righteous cease   SSA, baritone solo org (pf) 8:00 M;   Mercury MC 230

GORE, RICHARD T. 1908–
A child is born in Bethlehem (Ein kind geborn zu Bethlehem)
[canon] 3 eq unac 0:30 E;   in Four rounds, JF 9106
Come all you worthy gentlemen [canon] 4 eq unac 0:45 E;   in
Four rounds, JF 9106
Four rounds for Christmas (see individual titles for complete
information);   JF 9106
To us Christ comes winging / A Child is born in Bethlehem
/ Come all you worthy gentlemen / The new-born baby.
The new-born baby (Das neugeborene Kindelein) [canon] 4 eq
unac 1:10 E;   in Four rounds, JF 9106
To us Christ comes winging (Gottes Sohn ist kommen) [canon]
3 eq unac 1:00 E;   in Four rounds, JF 9106

GOSSWIN, ANTON c. 1540–1594
　Am Abend spät　　SSA unac 1:15 E-M;　in JöW, p 24
　Die Fassnacht ist ein schöne Zeit　　SSA unac 1:00 E;　in JöW,
　　p 135
　Ein guter Wein ist Lobes wert　　SSA unac 1:30 E-M;　in JöW,
　　p 122

GOUDIMEL, CLAUDE c. 1505–1572
　Which doth the loud noises of the seas　T: Ps LXVI　　SSAA
　　unac 1:30 M;　w/ 6 SATB settings in New York Public Library Publications I, p 13

GRANDI, ALESSANDRO DE' ?–1630
　Ave Regina coelorum (Sei gegrüsset uns)　　SSAA Bc 3:00 D;
　　in Das Chorwerk XL, p 13, Möseler

GREENE, MAURICE 1695–1755
　Blessed are those that are undefiled　T: Ps CXIX　　SA, SA
　　solo ad lib. org 8:00 E;　P Hinrichsen 51
　My lips shall speak of Thy praise, fr Blessed are they that are
　　undefiled　　SA pf 2:20 E;　OxCSM 1421

GRENON 15th C
　Je ne requier de ma dame　　SAA (SII) unac 1:10x2 E-M;　in
　　MET, p 33

GRIMM, HEINRICH c. 1593–1637
　Alleluja ist ein fröhlich Gesang　2 eq Bc 2:00 E-M;　w/Zu
　　dieser, in Bä 461
　Hosianna, dem Sohne David　2 eq Bc 3:45 M;　w/Wohlauf, in
　　Bä 458
　Machet die Tore weit　2 eq Bc 4:00 M;　w/Der Tag, in Bä 460
　Der Tag, der ist so freudenreich　2 eq Bc 0:50x2 4:00 M;
　　w/Machet, in Bä 460
　Wohlauf, wohlauf zu dieser Frist　2 eq Bc 2:45 M;　w/Hosi-
　　anna, in Bä 458
　Zu dieser osterlichen Zeit　2 eq Bc 4:00 M;　w/Alleluja, in Bä
　　461

GUARNIERI, MOZART CAMARGO 1907–
　Sinhô Láu (Mr. Nicolau)—Sinhô Láu quem falou (Nicolau
　　spoke of you)　　SSA unac 2:15 M;　Mercury MC 112

GUINNESS, KARIS 20th C
  Grey goose and gander [canon]   SA pf 1:00 E;   Joseph Williams St. Cecelia 27, no 25

GUMPELTZHAIMER, ADAM 1559–1625
  Die dunkle Nacht ist über uns gekommen   SSA unac 0:40x2
  E; in JöW, p 32
  Die finster Nacht nun vergeht mit Machte   SSA unac 0:45 E;
  in JöW, p 17
  (Go ye into all the world) [canon]   T: Matt. XXVIII: 19
  two eq unac 0:45 E; Con 98–1325
  Helft mir Gotts Güte preisen   SSAA unac 0:25x2 E-M;   in
  JöG, p 16
  Ich dank dir, lieber Herre   SSAA unac 0:15x2 0:25 E-M;   in
  JöG, p 67
  In meiner Not hoff ich auf Gott   SSA unac 0:20x2 0:30 E-M;
  in JöG, p 114
  Ist Gott für uns   SSA unac 0:30x2 E-M; in JöG, p 113
  Jesu, du armes Kindelein   SSA unac 1:00x2 M;   in JöG, p 17
  Lasst fröhlich nun uns singen   SSA unac 1:00x2 E-M;   in
  Eur, p 92
  Mit Fried und Freud fahr ich dahin   SSA unac 0:40x2 E;
  in JöG, p 57
  Nun freuet euch, ihr Arm und Reich   SSA unac 0:45x2 E-M;
  in JöG, p 14
  O Jesu Christ, verlass uns nicht   SSA unac 1:00 E-M;   in
  JöG, p 91
  Wacht auf, ihr lieben Vögelein   SSA unac 0:30x4 E-M;   in
  JöW, p 13

HAAS, JOSEPH 1879–
  Op. 73 Hymnen an den Frohsinn   SSA pf;   Schott

HAGIUS, CONRAD c. 1550–1620
  Du bist ein Gottesgabe   SSA unac 0:30x6 0:30x6 E-M;   in
  JöW, p 6
  Es stehet geschrieben   SSA unac 1:00 E; in JöW, p 137
  Gott geb uns heut ein gute Nacht   SSA unac 0:15x2 0:30;
  in JöG, p 78

Herzlich tut mich erfreuen   SSA unac 0:10x6 0:20x3 E;   in
JöW, p 52;   in Eur, p 67
O Mensch, betracht deiner Seelen Not   SSA unac 1:00 0:30x2
E-M;   in JöG, p 54

HAND, COLIN 1929–
Jolly Wat—The shepherd upon a hill he sat   T: Anon., 15th
   C   SSA pf descant recorders 11:30 E;   Ox 44.066

HANDEL, GEORG FRIEDRICH 1685–1759
Come ever smiling liberty, fr Judas Maccabaeus, in HäW XXII,
   p 54   SS pf 1:00 E;   N School 21
O lovely peace, fr Judas Maccabaeus, in HäW XXII, p 216   T:
   Thomas Morell   SA pf 3:45 E-M;   N School 111;   ES 1039

HÁNDL, JACOB 1550–1591
Christus factus est (Jesus Christ became)   T: Philippians II:
   8   SSAA unac 0:15 E;   in RWOM, ESV 869
Dicunt infantes, in DTÖ XII, p 172   SSSA unac 2:00 E-M;
   Bank
Gloria laus [prima pars] Israel es tu rex [secunda pars], in DTÖ
   XXIV, p 169   SSSA unac 1:00 1:00 E-M;   Bank
Pueri, concinite (Children, come), in DTÖ XII, p 167   SSAA
   unac 1:40 E-M;   trans and ed EHG, GS 8441
Regnum mundi, in DTÖ XXVI, p 210   SSAA unac 1:00 E-M;
   MCD 33
Replenti sunt omnes, in DTÖ XXX, p 152   T: Acts II: 4,
   11   SSAASSAA unac 1:15 E;   MCD 31
Trahe me post te (Let me run with you), in DTÖ XXVI, p 140
   SSSAA unac 1:00 M-D;   in Da, p 96;   Lat only, MCD 32
Virgines prudentes (O ye prudent virgins), in DTÖ XXIV, p 125
   T: Matt. XXV;   7   SSAASSAA 1:00 E;   in Da, p 108

HANSON, HOWARD 1896–
How excellent Thy name—O Lord our Lord   T: Ps VIII: 1,
   3–6   SSAA pf 4:00 M;   CF CM 6706

HARNISCH, OTT SIEGFRIED ?–1630
So wünsch ich ihr ein gute Nacht   SSA unac 0:15x4 0:20x2
   E-M;   in JöW, p 26

Weil ich gross Gunst trag zu der Kunst   SSA unac 0:45 E;
in JöW, p 4
Wenn ich seh deiner Äuglein Schein   SSA unac 0:25x4 E;
in JöW, p 65

Harrington, Henry 1727–1816

Harrington's hoop, seven catches and glees by Dr. Harrington
and others [not identified], ed and pf by John Edmunds
SSA;   Dow W 402
1. I gave her pig and I gave her pie   1:00 E
2. Go, gentle gales   0:45x2 0:45x2 E
3. Hark! ding, ding, ding!   0:50 E
4. Amo, amas, I love a lass   1:30 E
5. Poor Absalom is dead   1:50 E
6. Laughing catch   1:00 E
7. To all you ladies now at hand   0:40x4 E

Harris, Albert 1916–

The song of Koheleth—The words of Koheleth, the son of David
T: fr Ecclesiastes   SSAdiv Baritone solo, pf 6:00 M;
Mercury MC 198

Harris, Roy 1898–

They say that Susan has no heart for learning   T: Harris
SSA pf 2:15 M;   AM A–231
Whitman triptych   T: Walt Whitman;   GS 8503
1. I hear America singing—Ah, oh   SSSS unac 2:10 D
2. An evening lull—After a week of physical anguish
SSA unac 1:15 M
3. America—Center of equal daughters   SSAA unac
2:00 E

Hasler, see Hassler

Hasse, Johann Adolf 1699–1783

Miserere in D minor   T: Ps L   SSAA string orch 2:15 7:00
6:00 M;   ed EHG, choruses only, acc and SA soli available
fr publisher?, UPC 144;   ed H. S. Drinker, first chorus only,
UPC

HASSLER, HANS LEO 1564–1612

Benedictus (Selig ist), fr Missa quaternis   SSA unac 1:10 E-M; in JöG, p 136

Core mio (O my sweetheart)   SSAA unac 0:25x4 M; in Da, p 89

Crucifixus (Der um uns den Kreuzestod), fr Missae quaternis SSA unac 1:30 M; in JöG, p 37

Ecce non dormitabit (Siehe, es wird nicht schlafen)   SSA unac 2:00 M; in JöG, p 121

HAUPTMANN, MORITZ 1792–1868

Gebet [Op. 35, no 3]—Gott, deine Güte reicht so weit   SSA unac 2:10 E-M; in PAG, p 39; in PAS, p 48

HAUSSMANN, VALENTIN ?–after 1611

Annelein fein   SSAA unac 1:00x4 E-M; in JöW, p 69

Frisch ist mein Sinn   SSAA unac 1:45x2 E-M; in JöW, p 149

Ein lieblicher Wein   SSAA 0:40x6 E-M; in JöW, p 121

Mein trautes Liebelein   SSAA unac 0:30x8 E-M; in JöW, p 67

Mit Seufzen und mit Klag   SSAA unac 0:45x4 E-M; in JöW, p 103

Schätzlein, zu dir hat sich mein Herz gesellet   SSAA unac 0:30x2 0:30 E-M; in Eur, p 83

Soviel man Wasserwellen   SSA unac 0:45x6 E-M; in JöW, p 101

Wie sehr ich mich um Lieb nehm an   SSAA unac 1:00x8 E-M; in JöW, p 105

Zu ehren will ich singen   SSAA unac 0:30x2 E-M; in JöW, p 49

HAYDN, FRANZ JOSEPH 1732–1809 Timings and grades are not given as each may be considered 1–2 minutes and E or E-M

Die heiligen zehn Gebote (The holy ten commandments) [canons] 3–5 eq unac; MCD 10

    1. Du sollst an Einen Gott glauben (Thou in one God alone shalt believe)

    2. Du sollst den Namen Gottes (Thou shalt the name of God)

3. Du sollst Sonn- und Feyertag heiligen (Thou shalt keep the Sabbath)

4. Du sollst Vater und Mutter verehren (Thou thy father and mother shalt honor)

5. Du sollst nicht tödten (Thou shalt not murder)

6. Du sollst nicht Unkeuschheit treiben (Thou shalt not yield thee to lewdness)

7. Du sollst nicht stehlen (Thou shalt not pilfer)

8. Du sollst kein falsch Zeugniss geben (Thou shalt not false witness utter)

9. Du sollst nicht begehren deines Nächsten Weib (Thou shalt not go lusting for thy neighbor's wife)

10. Du sollst nicht begehren deines Nächsten Gut (Thou shalt not go lusting for thy neighbor's goods)

Ersatz (Love, gracious Goddess) [canon] T: Albert G. Latham 4 eq; Eng only, in Whit, p 19

Fester Sinn—Ein einzig böses Weib [canon] 3 eq; Fester Sinn —Der Fels, an dem die Wuth [original text missing], in Kanons, P 2965; Eng only (The problem solved—No perfect woman lives), T: Albert G. Latham, in Whit, p 5

Genuss des Augenblicks—Wohlgelebt, wer den Augenblick genoss [canon] 5 eq; in Kanons, P 2965

Guter Rat (His proper job) [canon] T: trans Albert G. Latham 8 eq; Eng only, 2 eq, in Whit, p 2

Herr Gänsewitz zu seinem Kammerdiener (To play the drum) [canon] T: Albert G. Latham 4 eq; Eng only, in Whit, p 17

Das Hexen-Einmal-Eins (The witch's once-times-one) [canon] T: trans Albert G. Latham 4 eq; Eng only, in Whit, p 14

Homo sum—O wollte doch der Mensch [canon] 4 eq; in Kanons, P 2965

Kanons von . . . ed Friedlaender (see individual titles for first lines and other editions when available); P 2965

1. Liebe
2. Sorge
3. Fester Sinn
4. Trost
5. Homo sum
6. Genuss des Augenblicks

Liebe—Sagt, was schwellt des Liedes Töne [canon] 3 eq; in Kanons, P 2965

Die liebe Maienzeit (The bird's song) [canon]   T: Albert G. Latham   4 eq;   Eng only, in Whit, p 15

Sorge—Kehre nicht in diesem Kreise [canon]   SAA;   in Kanons, P 2965

Trost—Des Lebens tiefstes Weh zerfliesst [canon]   3 eq;   in Kanons, P 2965

Wein, Liebe, Gesang (Soon will sorrow vanish) [canon]   T: Albert G. Latham   4 eq;   Eng only, in Whit, p 20

Weisheit (The wisest choice) [canon]   T: trans Albert G. Latham   4 eq;   Eng only, in Whit, p 15

Zuruf (Gifts in trust) [canon]   T: adapted Albert G. Latham   4 eq;   Eng only, in Whit, p 14

HAYDN, MICHAEL 1737–1806
Tenebrae factae sunt (Darkness was over all)   SSA org 2:30 E;   ed Reinhard Pauly, GS 10532

HAYES, PHILIP 1738–1797
Alleluia [canon]   8 eq unac 2:40 E;   w/Anon.:   Young, Norris: I said, Webbe: Glory, in SB Part song 85

HEMMER, EUGENE 1928–
Lord, who throughout these forty days   T: Claudia Herna-man, 1873   three eq org 2:00 E;   WLSM

HENDL, WALTER 1917–
Loneliness—No sky at all   T: Hanshin, trans Harold Hender-son   SSA pf 2:15 M-D;   CF CM 6654

A village where they ring no bells   T: Basho, 1644–1694, trans Harold Henderson   SSA pf 1:45 M;   CF CM 6653

HERRMANN, HUGO 1896–
Op. 74b Kleine Frauenchöre   SSA unac;   BB
  1. Rosenbrechen—Die Röslein sind zu brechen Zeit   0:15 E
  2. Kleiner Nachtgesang—Über allen Gipfeln ist Ruh   T: Goethe 1:10 M
  3. Kleine Humoreske—Man stirbt hier vor Langeweile T: Joachim Ringelnatz   0:30x2 0:15 M

Op. 85 Chorvariationen über die Sonnengesänge   T: Francis of Assisi, trans Franz Brentano and Max Lehrs   women's chorus, S(T) solo, harp (pf) 18:00;   BB [copy in New York Public Library]

HESELTINE, PHILIP [pseud. Peter Warlock] 1894–1930
Call for the robin-redbreast and the wren   T: John Webster, 1612   SSAA unac 1:30 M;   BoHa Winthrop Rogers 4246

HILTON, JOHN 1599–1657
Dear, may some other since not I   SSA unac 0:20x2 0:20x2 E; ed Arthur Goodchild, SB Ayres 6
Faint not lovers for denials   SSA unac 0:20x2 0:20x2 E;   ed Arthur Goodchild, SB Ayres 14
I heard a wither'd maid complain   SSA unac 0:40x2 0:40x2 E-M;   ed Arthur Goodchild, SB Ayres 10
My mistress frowns   SSA unac 0:15x2 0:15x2 E;   ed Arthur Goodchild, SB Ayres 2;   Eng Ger (Mein Lieb hat sich erzürnt), in Eur, p 53
Now is the summer springing   SSA unac 0:20x2 0:20x2 E-M; ed Arthur Goodchild, SB Ayres 19
O had not Venus been beguiled   SSA unac 0:20x2 0:25x2 E; ed Arthur Goodchild, SB Ayres 12
Phoebe tells me when I woo   SSA unac 0:20x2 0:20x2 E; ed Arthur Goodchild, SB Ayres 4
To sport our merry meeting   SSA unac 0:20x2 0:20x2 E; ed Arthur Goodchild, SB Ayres 1;   Ger only (Willkommen, holder Musikklang) in JöW, p 11
Willkommen, holder Musikklang, see To sport our merry meeting
You lovers that have loves astray   SSA unac 1:15x2 E-M; Eng Ger (Wenn Herzen auf Entfernung sinnen), in Eur, p 55

HINDEMITH, PAUL 1895–1963
Bastellied—Lasst uns alleine machen   T: Karl Schnog   SSA unac 0:50x2 E-M;   as supplement to La Revue musicale XI: 20 (Oct. 1930);   Schott
Mahnung an die Jungend, sich der Musik zu befleissigen (Admonishing young people to study music), fr Plöner Musiktag

T: Martin Agricola unison and SSA chorus, solo, speaker, strings, winds, percussion 35:00 E; Schott

A song of music—As donkeys bray   T: George Tyler   SSA orch (pf) 1:45 M; Schott

HINTON, J. ALBAN 19th–20th C

At Christmas be merry   SA pf (optional handbells or chime bars and recorders) 2:00 E; Ox

Rejoice and be merry [canon]   4 eq pf (optional handbells or chime bars and recorders) 3:45 E; Ox

HOFHAIMER, PAUL 1459–1537

Tu ne quaesieris (Ah, Leuconoe dear), fr Harmoniae poeticae, 1539   T: Quintus Horatius Flaccus: Odarum liber I, XI SSAA unac 0:20 E; in Da, p 8

Vitam quae faciant beatiorem (These are things that will make a life more happy), fr Harmoniae poeticae, 1539   T: Marcus Valerius Martialis: Epigrammaton liber: X, XLVII SSAA unac 0:20 E; in Da, p 9

HOLBORNE, WILLIAM flourished 1597

Change then, for lo she changeth, in EMS XXXVI, p 1   SSA unac 0:05x2 0:10x2 E; SB M 36/1

Gush forth my tears, in EMS XXXVI, p 9   SSA unac 0:15x2 0:15x2 E-M; SB M 36/5

Here rest my thoughts, in EMS XXXVI, p 5   SSA unac 0:15x2 0:15x2 E

Since Bonny-Boots was dead, in EMS XXXVI, p 2   SSA unac 0:20x2 0:20x2 E; SB 36/2

Sit still and stir not, in EMS XXXVI, p 11   SSA unac 0:15x2 0:20x2 E; SB M 36/6

Sweet, I grant, in EMS XXXVI, p 7   SSA unac 0:15x2 0:15x2 E; SB M 36/4

HOLST, GUSTAV 1874–1934

Ave Maria   SSAASSAA unac 5:00 E-M; Gray MS 312

Choral hymns from the Rig Veda, second group [Op. 26] orch (pf, violins ad lib.)

   1. To Varuna—O Varuna we offer up to thee a song SSA, SSA small chorus 7:00 E-M; Gray MS 284

2. To Agni—Burn up our sin   SSA 1:50 M;   Gray MS 285

3. Funeral chant—To those for whom the meath is poured   3 SA groups 3:00 M;   Gray MS 286

Pastoral—Early as I rose up   SSA, S solo unac 0:45x2;   SB Part songs 62

Seven part-songs for female voices and strings (pf) [Op. 44]   T: Robert Bridges

1. Say who is this   SSA 3:00 E;   N Trios 509

2. O love I complain   SSA, S solo 1:10 E;   N Trios 510

3. Angel spirits of sleep   SSAdiv 1:30 E;   N Trios 511

4. When first we met   SSA, S solo 1:30 E;   N Trios 512

5. Sorrow and joy   SSA 1:15 E;   N Trios 513

6. Love on my heart from heaven fell   SSA, S solo 1:25 E;   N Trios 514

7. Assemble all ye maidens   SSA, S solo 10:30 M;   N Trios 515

Songs from the Princess   T: Tennyson

1. Sweet and low   SSAASSAA unac 1:45 E;   N Trios 361

2. The splendour falls   SSAASSAA unac 1:30 E;   N Trios 362

3. Tears, idle tears   SSAA unac 2:00 E;   N Trios 363

4. O swallow   SSAA unac 1:15 E;   N Trios 364

5. Now sleeps the crimson petal   SSAA, S solo unac 1:30 E;   N Trios 365

The swallow leaves her nest   T: Thomas Lovell Beddoes   SSA unac 2:15 E;   ES 453

HONEGGER, ARTHUR 1892–1955

Cantique de Pâques—Alleluia Christ est ressuscité   SSA, SSA soli orch (pf) 7:15 E;   Rouart Lerolle 11475

HOVHANNES, ALAN 1911–

Op. 100, no 1a Ave Maria, fr Triptych [other compositions not for women's voices]   SSAA 2 oboes (trumpets or clarinets), 2 horns (trombones), harp (pf) 2:40 M;   vocal score, AM A–277;   score and parts, AM

HULSE, CAMIL VAN 1897–
  Psalm 150—Give praise to the Lord T: Ps CL   SSA org
  3:00 M;   WLSM

HUMPERDINCK, ENGELBERT 1854–1921
  (The sandman's song)—(I am the little sandman), fr Hänsel and
    Gretel T: Adelheid Wette   SA pf 2:45 E;   trans KKD,
    ES 1833

HUTCHINSON, FRANCIS [pseud. FRANCIS IRELAND] 1721–1780
  How sleep the brave T: fr Appolonian harmony, c. 1790
  SSA unac 2:30 E-M;   ed GWW, GS 10674

INCH, HERBERT 1904–
  Cradle song—Sweet dreams form a shade T: William Blake
  SSdivA unac 3:10 E-M;   Dow W 550

INGEGNERI, M. c. 1545–1592
  Vere languores nostros (Surely He hath borne our griefs) T:
    Isaiah LIII: 4   SSA unac 0:30 E;   ES 1506
  Virgo prudentissima   SSSA unac 2:30 M;   Bank

IRELAND, FRANCIS, see HUTCHINSON

ISAAC, HEINRICH c. 1450–1517
  Hör an mein Klag   SSA unac 1:00 E-M;   in Eur, p 68
  Innsbruck, ich muss dich lassen, in DTÖ XXVIII, p 83 [Isaac's
    text added by ed to this originally textless instrumental (?)
    setting]   SSAA unac 0:30 M;   in JöW, p 87

JACOB, GORDON 1895–
  The Babe so sweet—All holy angels sing T: Sidney Gray
    SdivSA unac 2:00 E;   Joseph Williams St. Cecilia Series 27,
    no 27
  Sisters awake! Close not your eyes T: Anon., 16th C   SSA
    unac 2:00 E;   OxCS 548

JACOPO DA BOLOGNA 14th C
  Non al suo amante   SA unac 2:00x2 0:15 M;   Éditions de
    l'oiseau lyre, 122 Rue de Grenelle, Paris;   in HAM I, p 52

JACOTIN [JACQUES GODEBRYE] c. 1445–1529
  Je suis déshéritée (I have lost all my fortune)   SA unac 1:45
    E-M;   ed David w/Certon: Je n'ose, Sermisy: Auprès, Cer-
    ton: Je suis, in MP 34

JEEP, JOHANN 1581–1644
  Mein Feinslieb, du hast mich gfangen   SSA unac 1:00x2 E;
    in Eur, p 65

JEUNE, CLAUDE LE, see LE JEUNE, CLAUDE

JONES, ROBERT flourished 1607
  Now have I learned, in EFL, Jones, p 54   SS lute (pf) 1:00x3
    E-M
  O I do love, in EMS XXXV, p 29   SSA unac 2:10 E-M;   SB
    M 35/6
  She only is the pride, in EMS XXXV, p 7   SSA unac 2:15
    E-M
  Since first disdain began to rise, in EFL, Jones, p 41   SS lute
    (pf) 1:00 E
  Sweet Kate, in EFL, Jones, p 5   SS lute (pf) 0:35x3 E;   2
    verses only, ed WW, w/Campian: The man of life upright,
    unison, lute (pf), in OxCSM 312
  Thine eyes so bright, in EMS XXXV, p 1   SSA unac 1:25
    E-M;   SB M 35/1

JOSEPH, J. M.
  Adam lay i-bounden, no 2 of Three old carols T: 15th C
    SSA unac 0:45 E-M;   OxCS 212

JOSQUIN see DESPRÉS, JOSQUIN

JOSTEN, WERNER 1888–1963
  Spring night—O'er the garden's scented bowers T: Eichen-
    dorff, trans Isabella Parker   SSA pf 2:10 E;   D 14109

KASTALSKY, ALEXANDER 1856–1926
(Now is Christ risen)   SSAA unac 1:00 M;   Gray CMR 642
(Open unto us)   SSAA unac 1:55 M;   T: Isabel Hapgood,
adapted Arthur W. Locke, Gray CMR 718

KAY, ULYSSES 1917–
Christmas carol [1943]—The kings they came   T: Sara Teas-
dale   SSA unac 2:30 M;   Peer WO 524

KINDERMANN, JOHANN ERASMUS 1616–1655
(Creator Spirit, by whose aid) Veni, Creator Spiritus, mentes   T:
Rhabanus Maurus (?)   SA 2 vio (flutes or oboes) Bc 1:00x3
E;   Eng only, trans Dryden, 1693, ed Fritz Oberdoerffer, Con
98–1482

KIRK, THERON 1919–
The Child and the lamb—Little lamb, who made thee?   T:
William Blake, 1757–1827   SSA unac 2:15 E;   JF 9290

KNAB, ARMIN 1881–1951
Drei Frauenchöre   T: Richard Billinger   SSA unac;
Schott
    1. Mariä Verkündigung—Und blicken die Fenster 2:25 E-M
    2. Die Heiligen—Vom Himmel die Heiligen steigen 3:00 M
    3. Die Lilie—Wie in der Keuschheit Kleide 1:50 M
Löwenzahn (Dandelion)—Löwenzahn, zünde deine Lichtlein
ein (Tell the time)   T: Antonia Ridge   SSA unac 0:10
0:45 E;   Eng Ger (included but not underlayed) Bosworth
1589. Obtain from Belwin, Rockville Center, L.I., NY

KNIGHTON, MERRILL 1904–
Fanfare and alleluia—Alleluia   SSAA unac 2:00 E;   Harold
Flammer 89167

KODÁLY, ZOLTÁN 1882–
(The angels and the shepherds) Angyalok és pásztorok—(Gloria!
in excelsis Deo! Waken from your sleep)   T: trans Elizabeth Lockwood   SA, SSA unac 3:00 E-M;   Eng only, BoHa
1717
Ave Maria   SSA unac 1:45 E-M;   BoHa 1711
(Christmas dance of the shepherds)—(Long I slumbered)   T:

Elizabeth Lockwood   SA piccolo 2:00x5 E-M;   BoHa 5172
(The deaf boatman)—(Good morning, boatman) T: trans
  Clement Rogers   SSA unac 0:45 E-M; Eng only, OxCS
  541
(Epiphany) Vizkereszt—(Bright and shining dawns this holy
  day) T: trans Elizabeth Lockwood   SSA unac 8:00 M;
  Eng only, BoHa 1712
(God's blacksmith)—(Plod along) T: trans Elizabeth Lock-
  wood   SSA unac 1:00 M; OxCS 535
(King Ladislaus' men [or] Magyars and Germans)—(Who are
  you) Ki, s ki népei vagytok T: trans Elizabeth Lockwood
  and Clement Rogers   SSAA unac 2:25 M; OxCS 550
(The Leveret) Nyúlacska—(Little Lev'ret, whither turn you?)
  T: trans Elizabeth Lockwood   SS unac 1:30 E-M; Eng
  only, BoHa 1713
(Whitsuntide)—A pünkösdnek jeles napján (When forty days
  were past and gone) T: Trans Elizabeth Lockwood and
  Clement Rogers   SSAA, S solo unac 7:00 M; OxCS 549

KOERT, see VAN KOERT

KOK, JAN 19th–20th C
  Round about, 34 original canons and rounds in 6 spirited classi-
    fications   3–5 eq unac 1:00–2:00 each E;   Dow W 401
  I. Come and join the singing
    1. Hey! Come and join the singing
    2. Rain, rain
    3. Oh, would I were where I would be!
    4. No matter how their lengths are now
    5. O sorrow, sorrow
    6. Laugh and the world laughs with you T: Ella Wheeler
      Wilcox
    7. Would that our lives could be
    8. Though the rose's perfume and bloom
    9. Just as steady as the sun
  II. Riddles
    10. To Helen I disclosed my soul
    11. Oh, hello! T: Jan Kok
    12. Of all the rounds

13. Home, come back home again
III. Shakespeare and Khayyam
14. When that I was and a little tiny boy   T: Shakespeare,
Twelfth night
15. Jog on the footpath way   T: Shakespeare, The winter's
tale
16. Of wisdom did I sow   T: Khayyam, trans Fitzgerald
17. The moving finger writes   T: Khayyam, trans Fitzgerald
18. Ah, my belov'd   T: Khayyam, trans Fitzgerald
IV. With a pack on the back
19. Keep on climbing
20. Come, sing along
21. Along life's road
22. No matter how the wind blows
23. Summer or winter, spring or fall
24. Oh, what the welcome rain can do   T: paraphrased fr
Eyrlis Riste McClish
V. Whimsies
25. My name is Yon Yonson
26. It was a dark and stormy night
27. I never saw a purple cow   T: Gelett Burgess
28. Billy in one of his nice new sashes   T: Harry Graham
VI. Sacred and seasonal
29. Glory to God in the highest   T: after Luke II: 14
30. Merry Christmas to you and to you
31. A merry Christmas this round
32. We clearly have reason to carol around
33. When Mary beheld the lone and empty tomb
34. Alleluia, amen

KRAFT, WALTER 1905–
Ach wie flüchtig, ach wie nichtig [canon]   T: Michael Franck
SSA unac 0:25x7 E;   in Kanonische, Bä 1776
Allein Gott in der Höh sei Ehr [canon]   T: Nikolaus Decius
SSA unac 0:30x4 E;   in Kanonische, Bä 1776
Auf meinen lieben Gott [canon]   SSAA unac 1:00x5 E;   in
Kanonische, Bä 1776

Christ ist erstanden [canon]   SSAA unac 1:45 E-M;   in Kanonische, Bä 1776

Erhalt uns, Herr [canon]   T: Martin Luther   SSA unac 0:20x3 E;   in Kanonische, Bä 1776

Erschienen ist der herrlich Tag [canon]   T: Nikolaus Herman   SSA unac 0:20x5 E-M;   in Kanonische, Bä 1776

Es woll uns Gott genädig sein [canon]   T: Martin Luther   SSA unac 1:15x3 M;   in Kanonische, Bä 1776

Gelobet seist du, Jesu Christ [canon]   SSA unac 0:25x5 E-M;   in Kanonische, Bä 1776

Herr, nun selbst den Wagen halt [canon]   T: after Huldreich Zwingli   SSA unac 0:20x3 E;   in Kanonische, Bä 1776

Ich singe dir mit Herz und Mund [canon]   T: Paul Gerhardt   SSA unac 0:20x18 E;   in Kanonische, Bä 1776

Ich wollt, dass ich daheime wär [canon]   T: Heinrich von Lauffenberg, 1430   SSSAA unac 0:20x12 E-M;   in Kanonische, Bä 1776

In allen meinen Taten [canon]   T: Paul Fleming   SSA unac 0:45x15 E-M;   in Kanonische, Bä 1776

Kanonische Choralmotetten für alle Kirchenzeiten und kirchlichen Feiern (see individual titles for complete information); Bä 1776

Nun komm der Heiden Heiland / Gelobet seist du, Jesu Christ / Vom Himmel hoch / Nun singet und seid froh / Wie schön leuchtet der Morgenstern / O Haupt voll Blut und Wunden / O Traurigkeit / Christ ist erstanden / Erschienen ist der herrlich Tag / Komm, heiliger Geist / Allein Gott in der Höh sei Ehr / Erhalt uns, Herr / Es woll uns Gott genädig sein / Lobt Gott, ihr frommen Christen / Herr, nun selbst den Wagen halt / Ich wollt, dass ich daheime wär / Ach wie flüchtig, ach wie nichtig / Liebster Jesu / Ich singe dir mit Herz und Mund / Lobe den Herren, den mächtigen König / Nun danket alle Gott / O Gott, du frommer Gott / In allen meinen Taten / Auf meinen lieben Gott.

Komm, heiliger Geist [canon]   SSA unac 1:00x3 E-M;   in Kanonische, Bä 1776

Liebster Jesu [canon]   T: Tobias Clausnitzer   SSA unac
1:30x3 E-M;   in Kanonische, Bä 1776

Lobe den Herren, den mächtigen König [canon]   T: Joachim
Neander   SSAA unac 1:15x5 E;   in Kanonische, Bä 1776

Lobt Gott, ihr frommen Christen [canon]   T: after Ludwig
Heilmann, 1523   SSA unac 1:15x6 E-M;   in Kanonische,
Bä 1776

Nun danket alle Gott [canon]   T: Martin Rinckart   SSAA
unac 1:15x3 E;   in Kanonische, Bä 1776

Nun komm der Heiden Heiland [canon]   SAA unac 0:30x5
E-M;   in Kanonische, Bä 1776

Nun singet und seid froh [canon]   SSA unac 0:20x4 E;   in
Kanonische, Bä 1776

O Gott, du frommer Gott [canon]   T: Johann Heermann
SSSA unac 1:30x8 E-M;   in Kanonische, Bä 1776

O Haupt voll Blut und Wunden [canon]   T: Paul Gerhardt
SAA unac 0:45x10 E;   in Kanonische, Bä 1776

O Traurigkeit! [canon]   T: Johann Rist   SSA unac 1:00x6
E-M;   in Kanonische, Bä 1776

Vom Himmel hoch [canon]   SSA unac 0:30x13 E;   in Kanonische, Bä 1776

Wie schön leuchtet der Morgenstern [canon]   T: Philipp
Nicolai   SSA unac 1:00x7 E-M;   in Kanonische, Bä 1776

KŘENEK, ERNST 1900–

The earth abideth [1960]   T: Ecclesiasticus I: 4, 5, 7   SSA
unac 1:12 E-M;   no 1 of Three motets, Rongwen

Fairies' song [1960]—You spotted snakes   T: Shakespeare
SSA unac 0:53 E-M;   no 1 of Three madrigals, Rongwen

Five prayers for women's voices over the Pater noster as cantus
firmus (Fünf Gebete) [1944]   T: John Donne, Ger trans by
Křenek   SSAA unac;   U 12270 LW
   [unison cantus firmus] Pater noster 0:50 M
   1. From being anxious (Dass Angst uns packt) 1:30 D
   2. From needing danger (Dass durch Gefahr) 1:00 D
   3. Through thy submitting all (Wie alles hin du gibst)
      1:25 D

65

> 4. Heare us, O heare us Lord (Hör uns, o hör uns, Gott!) 1:20 D
>
> 5. That learning, thine ambassador (Dass Wissen, dein Geschenk an uns) 1:36 D

The four sweet months [1960]—First, April, she with mellow showers   T: Robert Herrick   SSA unac 0:45 E-M;   no 2 of Three madrigals, Rongwen

Leviathan [1960]—The earth is full of thy riches   T: Ps CIV: 24-26   SSA unac 0:42 E;   no 3 of Three motets, Rongwen

Proprium Missae in festo SS. Innocentium [Op. 89]—Ex ore infantium   SSAA unac 8:00 M;   Mills 4010

Summer again [1960]—Summer is coming   T: Tennyson   SSA unac 1:05 M;   no 3 of Three madrigals, Rongwen

Three madrigals (each published separately, see individual titles for complete information)

> Fairies' song / The four sweet months / Summer again.

Three motets (each published separately, see individual titles for complete information)

> The earth abideth / To the sea in ships / Leviathan.

To the sea in ships [1960]—They that go down to the sea   T: Ps CVII: 23-26, 29   SSA unac 1:10 M;   no 2 of Three motets, Rongwen

Two choruses for women's voices a cappella on Elizabethan poems [1939, Op. 87]   SSAA unac;   obtain through composer, 10424 Pinyon Ave., Tujunga, Calif.

> 1. This life, which seems so fair   T: William Drummond 1:10 M-D
>
> 2. Verses—Even such is time   T: Sir Walter Raleigh 2:00 M-D

KRIEGER, ADAM 1634–1666

O schöne Schäferin (O pretty shepherdess), in DdT XIX, p 39 SS Bc 1:45 E;   in GM, p 265;   ed Woodside w/optional text added to bass line, W 2889

KUGELMANN, JOHANNES ?–1542

Gott Vater, Sohn, heiliger Geist   SSA unac 0:45x2 E;   in JöG, p 70

Grates nunc   SAA unac 1:25 M;   in MET, p 74

Ich dank dir fast, Gott Vater gut   SSA unac 0:30x3 E-M;   in
JöG, p 69

LAFAGE 1801–1862
Ave Regina   SSA pf 1:30 M;   Z, no 7

LAMB, HUBERT 1909–
Six scenes from the Protevangelion—The Protevangelion, an
historical account by James the Lesser   T: James the Lesser
SSAA orch 60:00 M;   Wellesley edition no 2, Wellesley College

LANDINI, FRANCESCO 1325–1397
Sy dolce non sono   SAA unac 3:00 M;   in HAM I, p 57
El mie dolce sospir   SAA(II) unac 1:05x2 M;   in MET, p 14

LANG, HANS 1897–
Op. 19 Vier Weihnachtslieder   T: F. P. Kürten   SSA unac;
each published separately, score and voice parts available,
Schott
    1. Zweig von Bethlehem—O Pilgerpaar, mach weit die Tür
    2. Maria Königin—O wohl dir, Königinne!
    3. Weihnachtslicht—Nun ward zu Trost uns allen
    4. Fünf Rosen—Fünf Rosen ging ich brechen
Op. 41 Zwei geistliche Lieder   SSA 3 vio, viola;   each pub-
lished separately, score and voice parts available, Schott
    1. Im Himmelreich ein Haus steht   T: Spervogel
    2. O Frau ob aller Frauen Schar   2:00 E-M
Op. 43 Zwei Motetten   SSA, S descant unac;   each published
separately, Schott
    1. Jubilate Deo (Jauchze, alle Welt)   T: Ps IX   2:20
    E-M
    2. Laudate Dominum (Singt ein Loblied)   T: Ps CXVII
    2:00 E-M

LANGIUS, GREGOR ?–1587
Allein das bittre Scheiden   SSA unac 0:30x2 E-M;   in JöW,
p 92

Lenz kommt herbei   SSA unac 0:45x3 E-M;   in JöW, p 34
Wenn ich nur hab dich   SSA unac 1:00x3 E-M;   in JöG,
p 117

LANGLAIS, JEAN 1907–
Regina caeli   2 eq org 0:40 E;   WLSM

LANTINS, ARNOLD DE flourished c. 1450
Puisque je voy [rondeau]   SAA(II) unac 2:00 M;   in HAM I,
p 75

LANTINS, HUGO DE flourished c. 1450
Ce ieusse fait [rondeau]   SAA(I) unac 1:30 M-D;   in HAM I,
p 76

LASSUS, ORLANDO DE 1530 or 1532–1594
Adoramus te [MaO 52 (43)], in LW I, p 57   SSA unac 1:00
E-M;   in Tov, p 8;   GS 5604;   ed ATD, ES 1508;   Lat Eng
(We adore Thee, O Christ) ed and trans Williams, ES 1284;
Lat Ger (Christe wir beten dich), in JöG, p 88
Adoramus te, Christe [MaO 53 (44)], in LW I, p 57   SSA unac
0:55 E-M;   w/Palestrina: Salve, Palestrina: Sub tuum, in
UPC 95;   w/Palestrina: Patres nostri [arr], in JF 6439;   in
Tov, p 9;   Lat Ger (Auf zum Kreuze), in PAG, p 9
Adoramus te, Christe (We adore thee, O Lord) [MaO 224 (177)],
in LW V, p 63   SSSAA unac 1:15 M-D;   ESV 890;   Lat
only, in GM, p 125
Agimus tibi gratias (Lob und Dank bringen wir) [MaO 55 (46)],
in LW I, p 59   SSA unac 1:15 M;   in JöG, p 86;   Lat only,
in Tov, p 6
Agimus tibi gratias [MaO 97 (74)], in LW I, p 131   SSAA
unac 1:00 E-M;   in Tov, p 27
Alleluja [MaO 68 (51)], in LW I, p 68   SSAA unac 1:00 M;
in Tov, p 26;   Lat Ger (Alleluja, Ruhm und Herrlichkeit),
in JöG, p 143
Beatus homo [MaO 2], in LW I, p 2   T: Proverbs III: 13,
14   SA unac 2:00 E;   no 2 in Cantiones, MCD 11;   Lat
Eng (Most happy), in Da, p 41
Beatus vir [MaO 1], in LW I, p 1   T: Ecclesiasticus XIV: 22
SA unac 1:40 E;   no 1 in Cantiones, MCD 11;   Bank

Benedictus, fr Missa pro defunctis, not in LW   SSA unac 1:00
  M;   in Ste, p 55;   in Tov, p 20

Cantiones duarum vocum [MaO 1–12], in LW I, pp 1–7 (see individual titles for complete information);   MCD 11

1. Beatus vir	7. Justi tulerunt spolia
2. Beatus homo	8. Sancti mei
3. Oculos non vidit	9. Qui vult venire
4. Justus cor suum tradet	10. Serve bone
5. Expectatio justorum	11. Fulgebant justi
6. Qui sequitur me	12. Sicut rosa

Cantiones sine texte. Fantasies, Ricercare for two voices or instruments [MaO 13–24], in LW I, p 8ff   SA(II) unac textless 12 pieces each 1–2 minutes M;   MCD 16

Cor meum, not in LW   T: Ps XXXVIII: 10   SSA unac
  1:30 M;   w/Tu exsurgens, in UPC 118

Expandi manus meas ad te, fr Psalmi penitentiales VII, not in
  LW   T: Ps CXLII: 4   SA unac 0:50 E;   in Tov, p 3

Exspectatio justorum [MaO 5], in LW I, p 3   T: Proverbs X:
  28–29   SA unac 1:10 M;   no 5 in Cantiones, MCD 11;
  Lat Eng (While the hoping), in Da, p 43;   Bank

Fulgebant justi [MaO 11], in LW I, p 6   T: Antiphon from
  the Old breviary   SA unac 1:40 M;   no 11 in Cantiones,
  MCD 11;   Bank

Gross ist der Herr [trans of Magnus Dominus], in LW XX, p 79
  T: Ps CXLIV: 3   SSA 1:00 E;   Ger only in JöG, p 140

Herr, der du meine Stärke bist [trans of Diligam te, Domine],
  in LW XX, p 67   T: Ps XVIII   SSA unac 1:15 E-M;
  Ger only in JöG, p 116

Hodie apparuit [MaO 197 (159)], in LW III, p 150   SSA unac
  0:55 E;   ed Rossini w/Anon.: Dies, in JF 6438;   in Tov,
  p 10;   Lat Eng (This glad day He appeared), ed and trans
  Williams, ES 1285;   Bank

In pace in idipsum dormiam [MaO 56 (47)], in LW I, p 59
  SSA unac 1:00 E-M;   in Tov, p 7;   Lat Ger (In Frieden will
  ich nun ruhen), in JöG, p 58;   Bank

Ipsa te cogat [MaO 488 (339)], in LW XIII, p 22   T: fr Hymn
  Jesu nostra redemptio   SA unac 1:30 E-M;   in Tov, p 4;
  ES 1995

69

Justi tulerunt spolia [MaO 7], in LW I, p 4   T: Wisdom X: 19–20   SA unac 1:20 E-M;   no 7 in Cantiones, MCD 11;   Bank

Justus cor suum tradet [MaO 4], in LW I, p 2   T: Ecclesiasticus XXXIX: 6   SA unac 1:30 E-M;   no 4 in Cantiones, MCD 11;   Bank

Non avertas faciem tuam (O hide not thy face), fr Psalmi penitentiales V, not in LW   T: Ps CII   SA unac 1:05 E-M; w/Tu exsurgens, in Two excerpts from Penitential psalm V, WMtH 2W 3397

Oculus non vidit [MaO 3], in LW I, p 2   T: Corinthians II: 9   SA unac 0:50 E;   in Tov, p 2;   no 3 in Cantiones, MCD 11;   Bank

Qui sequitur me [MaO 6], in LW I, p 3   T: John VIII: 12 SSA unac 1:20 M;   no 6 in Cantiones, MCD 11;   Lat Eng (Who followeth me), in Da, p 42;   Bank

Qui vult venire [Mao 9], in LW I, p 5   T: Matthew XVI: 24 SA unac 1:45 M;   no 9 in Cantiones, MCD 11;   Bank;   Lat Ger (Jeder, der mit mir will gehen), in PAG, p 8

Sancti mei [MaO 8], in LW I, p 4   T: Antiphon from an old breviary, see Wisdom X: 17   SA unac 1:45 E-M;   no 8 in Cantiones, MCD 11;   in Tov, p 5;   Bank

Schaff' mir doch Recht in Sachen mein (Judge me aright in my emprise) [trans of Judica me, Domine], in LW XX, p 71   T: Ps XXVI   SSA unac 1:00 M;   Ger Eng in Three psalms, MCD 21

Serve bone [MaO 10], in LW I, p 6   T: Matthew XXV: 23 SA unac 1:40 E-M;   no 10 in Cantiones, MCD 11;   Bank

Sicut rosa [MaO 12], in LW I, p 7   T: Antiphon from an old breviary   SA unac 1:40 E-M;   no 12 in Cantiones, MCD 11;   men's voices clefs, Bank

Straf mich, Herr, nicht im Eifermut [trans of Domine, ne in furore], in LW XX, p 76   T: Ps XXXVIII   SSA unac 0:30 E;   Ger only in JöG, p 101

Three psalms on texts and tunes from Caspar Ulenberg's Psalter (see individual titles for complete information);   MCD 21
    Schaff' mir doch Recht in Sachen / Vernimm, Herr, meine Wort' / Wir haben, Herr, mit unsern Ohren.

Tragico tecti syrmate (Tragical vestments cover us) [MaO 689
(468)], in LW XIX, p 53   SSSSAA unac 1:50 1:20 D;   in
Da, p 99

Tu exsurgens, not in LW   T: Ps CII: 13   SSA unac 1:30
M;   w/Lotti: Vere, in JF 6463; w/Lassus: Cor, in UPC
118;   w/Non avertas, in Two excerpts from Penitential psalm
V, WMtH 2W 3397

Vernimm, Herr, meine Wort' (Hear me, Lord, as I sing) [trans
of Verba mea auribus], in LW XX, p 62   T: Ps V   SSA
unac 0:50 M;   Ger Eng in Three psalms, MCD 21

Die Welt und all ihr Reichtum [trans of Domini est terra], in
LW XX, p 70   T: Ps XXIV   SSA unac 1:00 E-M;   Ger
only in JöG, p 141

Wie ein Hirsch gierlich schreien tut [trans of Quem ad modum
desiderat], in LW XX, p 21   T: Ps XLII   SSA unac 1:00
E-M;   Ger only in JöG, p 99

Wir haben, Herr, mit unsern Ohren (Oft hear we, Lord, with
ears attending) [trans of Deus, auribus nostris], in LW XX,
p 78   T: Ps XLIV   SSA unac 1:00 M;   Ger Eng in Three
psalms, MCD 21

LATHAM, WILLIAM P. 1917–
Sisters, awake—Sisters, awake! Close not your eyes   T: Anon.,
16th C   SSA pf 1:30 M;   Mercury MC 207

LAWES, HENRY 1595–1662
The captive lover—If my mistress fix her eye   SSA unac 0:40
E;   w/Martini: A measure, in Old airs and glees III, SB
Part song 88

Come, Cloris, hye we to the bow'r   SSA unac 0:40x2 E;
w/Gamble: Will Cloris, in Joseph Williams Series 17, no 19

View, Lisbia, view   T: verse 1 Anon., verse 2 Albert G. Latham   SSA unac 0:55x2 E-M;   OxJP XIII

LAWES, WILLIAM 1582–1645
Gather your rosebuds   SSA unac 3:00x2 E;   Ox 54.100

O my Clarissa   SSA unac 0:20x2 0:20 E;   OxJP XI

LECHNER, LEONHARD c. 1550–1606
Ach Lieb, ich muss dich lassen [based on Isaac: Innsbruck]
SSA unac 0:30x3 E-M;   in JöW, p 86

Christus ist für uns gestorben   SSAA unac 1:45 E-M;   in
JöG, p 35

Drei Volksliedsaetze (see individual titles for complete information);   P 4853
   Jagen, Hertzen und Federspiel / Gruen ist der Mai / Mein
   grosse Lieb, die macht mich blind.

Ein jeder meint, er sei der best   SSAA unac 1:30 E-M;   in
JöW, p 152

Elend bringt Pein dem Herzen mein   SSA unac 0:10x2 0:30
E;   in JöW, p 107

Freu dich heut und allezeit   SSAA unac 2:30 E-M;   in JöG,
p 45

Glück, führ zurück   SSA unac 1:00x2 E-M;   in JöW, p 85

Grün ist der Mai   SSAA unac 0:20x4 0:20x2 M;   in JöW,
p 43;   w/Jagen, Mein, in Drei Volksliedsaetze, P 4853

Gut Singer und ein Organist   SSA unac 1:15x2 E-M;   in
JöW, p 15;   1:15x3 in MET, p 95

Hört, was sich hat zutragen   SSAA unac 0:10x8 0:10x4 0:10x8
E-M;   in JöW, p 139

Jagen, Hetzen und Federspiel   SSA unac 0:10x6 0:10x3 E-M;
in JöW, p 55;   w/Grün, Mein, in Drei Volksliedsaetze, P
4853

Mein grosse Lieb, die macht mich blind   SSA unac 1:00x2 E;
in JöW, p 75;   w/Jagen, Grün, in Drei Volksliedsaetze, P
4853

Scheiden von Lieb und das tut weh   SSA unac 1:00x3 E-M;
in JöW, p 84

Was will ich mehr von ihr   SSAA unac 0:10x4 0:10x2 0:10x4
E-M;   in JöW, p 76

LECOUTEUX, HERBERT flourished 1550
Louange et glorie (Praising and glory) [composer questionable]
SSAA unac 0:15x2 0:50 M;   in Da, p 86

LE JEUNE, CLAUDE 1528–c. 1600
Le courant des eaux recherchant (When the streams resume
their flowing), fr Musique mesurée   T: Antoine de Baïf
SA unac 0:25 E-M;   in Da, p 11

D'une coline   SSA, later SSAII unac 1:15 M;   in HAM I,
p 149

Ma Mignonne (Liebchen fein)   SA unac 2:00 E;   in Eur, p 21
Ma Mignonne (Liebchen fein)   SSA unac 2:30 E-M;   in Eur,
  p 16
O Seigneur, j'espars jour et nuit (Lord my God, I cry day and
  night), fr Musique mesurée T: Agrippa d'Aubigné, after
  Ps LXXXVIII   SA unac 0:25 E-M;   in Da, p 11
Quand la terre au printemps (When the earth in springtime)
  T: Antoine de la Roche Chandieu   SSAA unac 1:00 M;
  in Da, p 80

LE MAISTRE, MATTHEUS ?–1577

Ein feste Burg ist unser Gott T: Ps XLVI   SSA unac 1:15
  M;   Kalmus;   in JöG, p 119;   in PAG, p 10
Gott sei gelobet und gebenedeiet   SSA unac 1:20 M;   in JöG,
  p 20
Die Wahrheit ist gen Himmel geflogen   SSA unac 1:10 E-M;
  in JöW, p 159

LENDVAI, ERWIN 1882–1949

Op. 5 Nippon. Eine Chorsuite . . . nach alt-japanischen Dicht-
  ungen (A choral suite after old Japanese poems) unac;   Simrock

  1. Nippon—Das Land Yamato T: Ohotomo no Sukune
     Yakamochi   SSAAdiv 2:00 E
  2. Heimwärts—Die Blumen blüh'n T: Ise   SSAA
     1:15 E-M
  3. Komm einmal noch T: Idzumi Shikibu   SSAA
     1:45 E-M
  4. Der Mond—Wie die Wolken er zerbricht T: Ischi-
     kawa   SSSAAAdiv 1:30 M
  5. Der Frühling kam T: Narihira   SSAA 1:15 E
  6. Verträumtes Leben—Die Blumen blühten in lokkenden
     Farben T: Onono Komachi   SSSAA, S solo 1:15 M
  7. Sommerduft—Die nacht ist dunkel T: Ohichikafuhi
     no Mitsune   SSSAA 1:45 E-M
  8. Am heiligen See—Blüten schneien T: Ohotsuno Ozi
     SSSSAAAA 1:30 E-M
Op. 18 Fünfstimmige Frauenchöre ohne Begleitung (Five-voice
  women's choruses without accompaniment) T: Wilhelm

Conrad Gomoll   SSSAA unac M;   score and voice parts
available, Simrock
1. Licht!—Hell über Berg 3:00
2. Im Frieden der Nacht—Wenn all' die abertausend
   Lichtlein 1:30
3. Die Jungend sang im Garten 2:30
4. Sils Maria—Umspannt vom leuchtenden Aetherblau
   0:45
5. Lerchenlied—Helles Klingen in den Lüften 2:30
Op. 20 Jungbrunnen. Ein Liederkreis in deutscher Art   T:
E. A. Herrmann   SSA small orch (pf) 33:00 E-M;   score,
I parts, pf score, voice parts available, Simrock

LEONINUS flourished before 1163
Haec Dies   SA(I) unac 2:30 M;   in Ste, p 4

LEVY, ERNST 1895–
Hear, ye children   T: Proverbs IV: 1, 7–8   SSASSA unac
5:00 M;   BCS 1

LISZT, FRANZ 1811–1886
(Alleluia! Let all mankind rejoice), fr Christus   SSAA org
1:45 E;   trans Helen Dickinson, Gray Sacred choruses 31

LOCATELLO, GIOVANNI BATTISTA 16th C
Die Äuglein leuchten   SSA unac 0:30x8 E;   in JöW, p 71

LOCKE, MATTHEW 1632–1677
Ne'er trouble thyself   T: fr J. Gamble's Airs, 1659   SSA
unac 0:50x2 E;   in OxJP 6
Praise our Lord, all ye gentiles   SSA pf 0:50 E;   OxJP 9
Since by wealth   SSA unac 0:40 E;   OxJP 7

LOCKWOOD, NORMAND 1906–
The birth of Moses—And Pharaoh charged   T: fr Exodus
SSA pf flute 6:00 D;   Mercury MC 140

LOEFFLER, CHARLES MARTIN 1861–1935
Psalm 127 [Op. 3]—By the rivers of Babylon   SSAA org (pf)
harp 2 flutes cello 11:00 E-M;   keyboard and voices only, GS

LONDON, EDWIN 1929–
  Five haiku   T: trans Harold G. Henderson   SSAAdiv unac
  4:00 M-D;   AM A-374
    1. Leaves—The winds that blow   T: Natsume Sōseki,
       1867–1916
    2. In the moonlight—They look like men   T: Masaoka
       Shiki, 1867–1902
    3. A spring day—A day of spring   T: Masaoka Shiki
    4. The whale—A whale, down it goes   T: Taniguchi
       Buson, 1715–1783
    5. At the year's end—The old year goes away   T: Sōin,
       late 18th C

LOTTI, ANTONIO c. 1667–1740
  Agnus Dei (Lamb of God), fr Mass VII, in DdT LX, p 114
    SSAA unac 1:10 M;   ed Talmadge, ES 1949
  Vere languores nostros—   T: Isaiah LIII: 4   SSA unac
    1:45 E-M;   Lat Ger (Alle die tiefen Qualen) in JöG, p 24;
    Lat Ger (Alle die tiefen Qualen) in PAS, p 1;   Lat Ger
    (Alle die tiefen Qualen) in PAG, p 12;   ed Saar, Lat Eng
    (He surely hath borne our griefs) D 14.205;   Lat only
    w/Lassus: Tu, in JF 6463

LÜBECK, VINCENT 1654–1740
  Weihnachtskantate: Willkommen süsser Bräutigam (Christmas
    cantata: Welcome, thou King of glory)—Willkommen süsser
    Bräutigam (O welcome Bridegroom dear)   T: Johann Rist,
    1607–1667   SS(SA), SS soli, Vio I and II (2 flutes, oboes, or
    recorders) Bc 10:00 E;   trans Stephan, ed Oberdoerffer w/op-
    tional Bass voice, Con 97–6379 (score), Con 97–6385 (chorus
    part), Con 97–6386 (violins), Con 97–6387 (cello);   ed Weiss
    w/optional Bass voice, Merseberger

LUENING, OTTO 1900–
  If that high world   T: Byron   SSA unac 2:20 M;   BoHa
    Arrow
  Sun of the sleepless   T: Byron   SSA unac 2:00 M;   Row
    248

LUKAČIĆ, IVAN 1574?–1607
Odabrani Moteti (Ausgewählte geistliche Konzerte) "Sacrae cantiones" (1620) ed Dr. Dragan Plamenac III: Orantibus in loco isto   SA accompanied / V. Vesi, sponsa Christi AA accompanied / VIII. Ex ore infantium et lactentium SSS accompanied; Published Izdanja Hrvatskog Glaxben Zavoda Zagred [copy in Columbia University lib]

LUZZASCHI, LUZZASCO ?–c. 1607
Cor mio, deh non languire   SS Bc 3:00 D; in MET, p 107

LYBBERT, DONALD 1923–
Austro terris influente T: fr Ms Pl. 29.1   SSAA pf 3:45 8:50 4:00 M-D [each section may be performed separately]; Mercury MC 416

McDONALD, HARL 1899–
Dirge for two veterans—The last sunbeam falls T: Walt Whitman   SSAA pf 7:30 M; Elkan-Vogel

McLAUGHLIN, MARIAN 1923–
Torches T: Galician   SSA pf 3:00 E; GS Lawson-Gould 924

MACHAULT 1300?–1377
Quant Théseus (When Jason)   SA unac 0:45x2 1:00 M; in Lehman Engel, Three centuries of choral music, I, p 6, Harold Flammer
S'il estoit nulz [isorhythmic motet]   SAI 2:30 E-M; in HAM I, p 46

MAHLER, GUSTAV 1860–1911
(Bell chorus), fr Symphony V, 3d movement—Es sungen drei Engel einen (Three angels a sweet carol sang) T: fr Knaben Wunderhorn   SSAA, A solo, boys unison pf, glockenspiel, triangle 5:30 M; AJ 31

MAHU, STEPHAN ?–before 1544?
Christ ist erstanden   SSSAA unac 1:30 M-D; lowest voice transposed up one octave, in Lei I, p 3

MANZIARLY, MARCELLE DE 1899–
  Venez, venez, pastoureaux (O come, O come, shepherds all), no
  3 fr L'Adoration des Berger   T: composer   SS, A ad lib.
  pf 2:10 M;   acc missing, Rouart

MARCELLO, BENEDETTO 1686–1739
  (And with songs I will celebrate), fr 50 Salmi di Davide   T: Ps
  XIII: 6   SA pf (org) 2:30 E;   ed Richard Weinhorst,
  trans Stevens, Con 98–1047
  (As the hart panteth), fr 50 Salmi di Davide   T: Ps XLII
  SS(A) pf (org) 4:00 E-M;   ed W. H. Longhurst, N Choral song
  45
  (Give ear unto me), fr 50 Salmi di Davide   T: Ps XVII
  SS(A) pf (org) 2:15x2 1:00 E;   ed Vincent Novello, N School
  467
  (Oh, hold thou me up), fr 50 Salmi di Davide   T: Ps XVII:
  5–6   SA pf (org) 4:00 E;   ed Richard Weinhorst, trans
  Stevens, Con 98–1046
  (O Lord, deliver me), fr 50 Salmi di Davide   T: Ps VII: 1–2
  SA pf (org) 2:00 M;   ed Richard Weinhorst, trans Stevens,
  Con 98–1044

MARENZIO, LUCA 1553–1599
  Amatemi ben mio (Filli mich jetzund liebet)   SSA unac
  1:00x2 E;   in Eur, p 11
  Kommt, ihr lieblichen Stimmen alle   SSB unac 0:20x8 E;
  lowest voice transposed up one octave, SSA, in JöW, p 8
  Mein edle Kaiserinne   SSB unac 0:25x3 M;   lowest voice
  transposed up one octave, SSA, in JöW, p 72
  Occhi dolci e soavi   SSB unac 1:00x2 E-M;   It Ger (Gross
  Leid und bittres Klagen), lowest voice transposed up one oc-
  tave, SSA, in Eur, p 9;   Ger only (O holdseliges Herze), low-
  est voice transposed up one octave, SSA, in JöW, p 100
  O holdseliges Herze, see Occhi dolci e soavi
  Von eim fliessenden Brunnen   SSA unac 0:25x6 E-M;   in
  JöW, p 23
  Wo ist der Tag hinkommen?   SSA unac 0:30x4 E-M;   in
  JöW, p 31

MARTINI, GIOVANNI BATTISTA 1706–1784
In monte Oliveti   SSA unac 1:00 E;   Lat Eng (On the Mount
of Olives), ES Dunstan 1283;   Lat Ger (Als Jesus lag am
Ölberg), in JöG, p 30
(A measure to pleasure your leisure—With rhymes that are
witty) T: Clifford Bax [not original]   SSA unac 0:25
0:25x2 E-M;   w/Lawes: The captive, in SB Part songs 88
O salutaris hostia (Blessed are they that do Thy will)   SSA
unac 1:30 E;   Eng only, w/Menegali: Jesu, in ES 1888

MARTINU, BOHUSLAV 1890–1955
Bolavé srdečko (The aching heart)—Oh, maměnko (Oh, my
heart is aching) T: Eng by Nancy Bush   SSA unac 2:00
M;   BoHa 1947
Chudá děvčica (The penniless sweetheart)—Kdybych já byl
(Like a bird flying) T: Eng by Nancy Bush   SSA unac
0:30x2 0:45 E-M;   BoHa 1948
Hlásání Pasaček (Shepherd's song)—Hej! Halilalou! Mářo!
Mařenko Zikmundová (Hey! Halilalou! Anna, listen and come
when I call) T: Eng by Nancy Bush   SSAA unac 2:00
E-M;   BoHa 1946
Na nebe vstoupení Páně (The Ascension)—Když milý pan Ježíš
(When our dear Lord) T: Eng by Nancy Bush   SSA, vio
1:15x2 1:00 M;   BoHa 1944
Narození Páně (The birth of our Lord)—Prýščí se studená (Cold
from its rocky bed) T: Eng by Nancy Bush   SSA, vio
0:12x2 0:20x2 0:50 E-M;   BoHa 1945

MARX, KARL 1897–
Abendständchen—Hör, es klagt die Flöte wieder T: Clemens
Brentano   SSA recorder 2:30 M;   w/Das kleine, Himmels-
Au, in Kleine Kantaten, Bä 2710
Abendständchen—Und jetzo kommt die Nacht herbei   SSA
unac 0:20x3 E;   in Lieber Nachbar, Alte, Bä 3171
Dass zwei sich herzlich lieben T: Hermann Claudius   SSA
unac 0:20x3 E;   in Lieber Nachbar, Alte, Bä 3171
Drescherlied—Klipp und klapp T: Heinrich Voss, 1751–1826
SSA flute, and percussion I ad lib. 0:20x4 E;   in Lieber
Nachbar, Alte, Bä 3171

Es flog ein Täublein weise   T: Walther Hensel   SSA unac
0:35x5 E; in Lieber Nachbar, Alte, Bä 3171

Festliches Lied—Einmal nur in unserm Leben   T: Goethe
SSA unac 1:20 E; in Lieber Nachbar, Alte, Bä 3171

Freudvoll und liedvoll   T: Goethe   SSA unac 0:30 E;   in
Lieber Nachbar, Alte, Bä 3171

Ein getreues Herze wissen   T: Paul Fleming, 1609–1640
SAA unac 0:25x6 E; in Lieber Nachbar, Alte, Bä 3171

Halt hoch dich über dem Leben [Op. 58]—Es schauert der Wald
vor Lust   T: Eichendorff   SSSAA, soprano and alto recorders, pf, drum ad lib., vio I, vio II, viola, cello   15:00 M;
Bä 3884

Die heiligen drei König   SSA unac 0:20x5 E;   in Lieber
Nachbar, Alte, Bä 3171

Herr, lass dir gefallen   T: Goethe   SSA unac 1:30 E-M;
in Lieber Nachbar, Alte, Bä 3171

Himmels-Aug, licht und blau   SA, flute, vio   8:00 E;   w/
Abendständchen, Das kleine, in Kleine Kantaten, Bä 2710

Ho, ho, ho   SSA unac 0:25x3 E; in Lieber Nachbar, Alte,
Bä 3171

Hochzeitsgesang—Ihr in der Liebe geborgen   T: Bernt von
Heileler   SAA unac 0:30x2 E;   in Lieber Nachbar, Alte,
Bä 3171

Ich hab kein Geld   SSA unac 0:30x3 E;   in Lieber Nachbar,
Alte, Bä 3171

Ich hört ein Sichlein rauschen   T: Ludwig Uhland   SA
unac 0:15x3 E; in Lieber Nachbar, Alte, Bä 3171

Ihr kleinen Vögelein   T: Angelus Silesius   SSA, flute, oboe
(vio or alto flute), guitar (lute) ad lib., vio, cello 2:30 E-M;
Bä 3940

Ihr müsst wandern unermüdlich [Op. 57a]—Zögert Sonne noch
am Rande   T: Hans Carossa   SSA, recorder quartet, 2
flutes, xylophone, glockenspiel, percussion, 2 vio I, 2 vio II,
viola, cello, bass ad lib. 7:30 E-M;   Bä 3649

Jeden Morgen geht die Sonne auf   T: Hermann Claudius
SSA unac 0:25x4 E; in Lieber Nachbar, Alte, Bä 3171

Kehraus—Geht heim, ihr Mädchen   T: fr Knaben Wunder-
horn   SSA unac 0:15x2 0:10 E;   in Lieber Nachbar, Alte,
Bä 3171
Das kleine Federspiel—Wohlauf, ihr klein Waldvögelein   T:
fr Knaben Wunderhorn   SSA, 2 recorders 0:15x2 (I), 0:35
(SA), 0:15x2 (I), 0:35 (SA), 0:40 (I), 0:40 (SSA), 0:15x2 (I), 0:25
(SSA), 0:20 (I), 0:30 (SA), 0:20 (I), 0:40 (SSA and I) M;
w/Abendständchen, Himmels-Au, in Kleine Kantaten, Bä
2710
Kleine Kantate—Jeden Morgen geht die Sonne auf   T: Her-
mann Claudius   3 eq four I 2:45 E-M;   Bä 2716
Lieber Nachbar   SSA unac 0:20x3 E;   in Lieber Nachbar,
Alte, Bä 3171
Lieber Nachbar, Alte und neue Lieder in Sätzen für gleiche
Stimme (see individual titles for complete information);   Bä
3171
    Jeden Morgen geht die Sonne auf / Zum neuen Jahr / Ho,
    ho, ho / Ich hab kein Geld / Der Maien / Ich hört ein Sich-
    lein rauschen / Pfirsichblüte / Wenn ich ein Vöglein war /
    Freudvoll und leidvoll / Dass zwei sich herzlich lieben / Ein
    getreues Herze wissen / Hochzeitsgesang / Der Mensch hat
    nichts so eigen / Sommerliches Land / Wia der Acker /
    Drescherlied / O Tannenbaum / Es flog ein Täublein weisse
    / Die zwei Hirten in der Christnacht / Die heiligen drei
    König / Und in dem Schneegebirge / Kehraus / Festliches
    Lied / Abendständchen / Lieber Nachbar / Herr, lass dir
    gefallen / Musik, du edle Trösterin.
Der Maien   T: Hans Sachs, 1562   SSA unac 0:30x2 E;   in
Lieber Nachbar, Alte, Bä 3171
Der Mensch hat nichts so eigen   T: Simon Dach   SSA unac
0:15x8 E;   in Lieber Nachbar, Alte, Bä 3171
Musik, du edle Trösterin   SSA unac 0:20 E-M;   in Lieber
Nachbar, Alte, Bä 3171
O Tannenbaum   SAA unac 0:20x3 E;   in Lieber Nachbar,
Alte, Bä 3171
Pfirsichblüte   T: Klabund   SSA unac 0:40 E;   in Lieber
Nachbar, Alte, Bä 3171

Sommerliches Land—Grün wogt das Korn im Ackergrund   T:
Martha Müller-Zitzke   SAA unac 1:00 E-M;   in Lieber
Nachbar, Alte, Bä 3171
Und in dem Schneegebirge   SSA unac 0:20x5 E;   in Lieber
Nachbar, Alte, Bä 3171
Wenn ich ein Vöglein wär   SAA unac 0:15x3 E;   in Lieber
Nachbar, Alte, Bä 3171
Wia der Acker   SSA unac 0:15x2 E;   in Lieber Nachbar,
Alte, Bä 3171
Zum neuen Jahr—Wie heimlicher Weise ein Engelein   T:
Mörike   SAA unac 0:30x2 E;   in Lieber Nachbar, Alte,
Bä 3171
Die zwei Hirten in der Christnacht—Ich will dem Knäblein   T:
fr Knaben Wunderhorn   SSA unac 0:20x4 E;   in Lieber
Nachbar, Alte, Bä 3171

MASSENTIO, DOMENICO 16th–17th C
Sancta Maria   2 eq Bc 2:15 E-M;   Canticum vetus 8, Schott

MEDICI, LORENZO 1449–1492
Es liebt mir das Jagen   SSA unac 0:35x6 M;   in JöW, p 56
Mein Schätzlein ist von Flandern   SSB unac 0:25x6 E-M;
lowest voice transposed up one octave, SSA, in JöW, p 124

MEGAREY, ANNE 19th–20th C
Gloria in excelsis Deo—Glory to God   SSAA unac 1:00 E;
OxCS 523

MENDELSSOHN-BARTHOLDY, FELIX 1809–1847
In His hand, fr 95th Psalm, Come let us sing   T: Ps XCV: 4
SS pf 4:10 E;   N School songs 886
Laudate pueri [Op. 39, no 2]   T: Ps CIII: 21;   CXII
SSA, SSA soli org 4:30 E-M;   ed and trans Harold Aks, Lat
Eng (Praise ye the Lord), AJ 81;   trans Walmisley, Lat Eng
(O praise the Lord), N Trios 57;   Lat Eng (Ye sons of Israel),
ES 1839
Lift thine eyes to the mountains, fr Elijah   T: Ps CXXI:
1–3   SSA unac 1:20 E-M;   ed HC-L, ES 1017;   GS 26;
N Musical times 388;   D 820;   Ger only (Hebe deine Augen

auf), in PAS, p 25; Ger only (Hebe deine Augen auf), in PAG, p 30

Surrexit Pastor bonus (O Lord, thou hast searched me out) [Op. 39, no 3] T: Ps CXXXIX: 1, 6–8 SSAA, SSAA soli org 8:15 E-M; trans Walmisley, N Trio 58

Three motets [Op. 39] (see individual titles for complete information)

Veni Domine / Laudate pueri / Surrexit Pastor bonus.

Through the house give glimmering light, Finale from a Midsummer night's dream T: Shakespeare SSA, S solo, 2 speakers orch (pf) 4:00 E; N Octavo choruses 641

Veni Domine [Op. 39, no 1] T: Ps CII: 1–2 SSA org 3:30 M; ed and trans Harold Aks, Lat Eng (Hear our prayer, O Lord), AJ 82; trans Walmisley, Lat Eng (Hear my prayer), N Trios 56; Lat Ger (Herr, erhöre uns), BH

You spotted snakes, with double tongue, fr a Midsummer night's dream, Act II, scene 3 T: Shakespeare SSAA, SS soli, 1 speaker, orch (pf) 4:30 M; N Octavo choruses 640

MENEGALI, MARTIN J. 1784–1851

Jesu, Salvator mundi (Blessed are the merciful) English T: Matthew V: 7 SSA unac 0:30 E; in RWOM, ESV 869; Eng only w/Martini: O salutaris, in ES 1888

MENNIN, PETER 1923–

Bought locks—The golden hair that Gulla wears T: Martial, c. 40–c. 102, trans Sir John Harington SSA pf 2:00 E-M; CF CM 6484

The people that walked in darkness, fr The Christmas story T: Isaiah IX: 2 SSAA orch (pf) 3:00 M; CF CM 7044

MERULA, TARQUINIO c. 1590–1655

Omnes consurgite SS org Lat 4:15 E-M; w/Menichetti: Media vida [not included in this List], in Casa editrice 6041 [obtain through WLSM]

MEYEROWITZ, JAN 1913–

Two litanies [1952]; Broude BB 125

   1. In my orchard, pearl'd with dew T: after Sister Bertken SSA pf 3:00 D

2. If I have my Jesus   T: after Novalis   SSA, SA soli,
   pf 2:10 D

MICHEELSEN, HANS FRIEDRICH 1902–
   Alle gute Gabe   T: James I: 17   SSA unac 1:00 M;   Bä
   3188;   in Hamburger . . . IV, Bä 3180
   Als unser Herr in den Garten ging   SSA unac 1:00 3:00 1:30
   M;   Bä 1570;   in Hamburger . . . III, Bä 1333
   Das ist gewisslich wahr   T: I. Timothy I: 15   SSA unac
   1:30 M;   Bä 3195;   in Hamburger . . . IV, Bä 3180
   Den aber, der eine kleine Zeit, niedriger gewesen ist   T: He-
   brews II: 9   SSA unac 1:00 M;   Bä 3185;   in Ham-
   burger . . . IV, Bä 3180
   Denn von ihm durch ihn und zu ihm sind alle Dinge   T: Ro-
   mans XI: 36   SSA unac M;   Bä 3190;   in Hamburger
   . . . IV, Bä 3180
   Es ist erschienen die heilsame Gnade   T: Titus II: 11
   SSA unac 1:45 E-M;   Bä 3183;   in Hamburger . . . IV, Bä
   3180
   Freuet euch in dem Herrn allewege   T: Philippians IV: 4
   SSA unac 1:00 M;   Bä 3182;   in Hamburger . . . IV, Bä 3180
   Fürwahr, Er trug unsere Krankheit   T: Isaiah LIII: 4–5
   SSA unac 2:00 E;   Bä 3186;   in Hamburger . . . IV, Bä 3180
   Gott aber kann machen, das allerlei Gnade   T: II. Corin-
   thians IX: 8   SSA unac 1:30 E-M;   Bä 3192;   in Ham-
   burger . . . IV, Bä 3180
   Gott ist Liebe   T: I. John IV: 16   SSA 0:20x2 0:25 M;
   w/Leben wir, in Bä 3191;   in Hamburger . . . IV, Bä 3180
   Hamburger Motettenbuch, Heft III, Choralmotetten (see individual titles for complete information);   complete, Bä 1333;
   also published separately
      Hinunter ist der Sonne Schein / Mit Fried und Freud ich
      fahr dahin / Als unser Herr in den Garten ging.
   Hamburger Motettenbuch, Heft IV, Epistelsprüche (see individual titles for complete information);   complete, Bä 3180;
   also published separately
      Die Nacht ist vorgerückt / Freuet euch in dem Herrn
      allewege / Es ist erschienen die heilsame Gnade / Mache

dich auf, werde licht / Den aber, der eine kleine Zeit niedriger gewesen ist / Fürwahr, Er trug unsere Krankheit / Nun aber ist Christus auferstanden / Alle gute Gabe / Lasset uns rechschaffen sein in der Liebe / Denn von ihm / Leben wir, so leben wir dem Herrn / Gott aber kann machen, dass allerlei Gnade / Unser Wandel ist im Himmel / Lasset das Wort Christi unter euch reichlich wohnen / Das ist gewisslich wahr.

Hinunter ist der Sonne Schein   SSA unac 0:40 0:30 0:40 0:40 0:50 M;   Bä 1568;   in Hamburger . . . III, Bä 1333

Lasset das Wort Christi unter euch reichlich wohnen   T: Colossians III: 16   SSA unac 2:00 M;   Bä 3194;   in Hamburger . . . IV, Bä 3180

Lasset uns rechtschaffen sein in der Liebe   T: Ephesians IV: 15   SSA unac 1:00 M;   Bä 3189;   in Hamburger . . . IV, Bä 3180

Leben wir, so leben wir dem Herrn   T: Romans XIV: 8   SSA unac 1:00 M;   w/Gott ist Liebe, in Bä 3191;   in Hamburger . . . IV, Bä 3180

Mache dich auf, werde licht   T: Isaiah LX: 1   SSA unac 1:30x2 0:30 E-M;   Bä 3184;   in Hamburger . . . IV, Bä 3180

Mit Fried und Freud ich fahr dahin   SSA unac 0:30 0:45 0:45 0:40 0:40 M;   Bä 1569;   in Hamburger . . . III, Bä 1333

Die Nacht ist vorgerückt   T: Romans XIII: 12   SSA unac 2:00 E-M;   Bä 3181;   in Hamburger . . . IV, Bä 3180

Nun aber ist Christus auferstanden   T: I. Corinthians XV: 20, 55, 57   SSA unac 1:15 E-M;   Bä 3187;   in Hamburger . . . IV, Bä 3180

Unser Wandel ist im Himmel   T: Philippians III: 20   SSA unac 1:45 E-M;   Bä 3193;   in Hamburger . . . IV, Bä 3180

MILFORD, ROBIN 1903–
Hear me, O God   T: Ben Jonson   SA org (pf) 3:00 E;   OxCS 200

MILHAUD, DARIUS 1892–
Cantata from Proverbs—Who crieth: "Woe"?   T: Proverbs

XXIII: 29–35; IX: 13–18; XXXI: 10–31   SSA keyboard (harp), oboe, cello 3:10 1:15 4:00 D;   Mercury MC 189

Monteverdi, Claudio 1567–1648
   Angelus ad pastores, in MoTO XIV, p 36   SSA unac 1:05
      E-M;   w/Monteverdi: Hodie, in MCD 24;   Bank
   As from the earth a flower grows, see Si come crescon alla terra
   Ave Maria, in MoTO XIV, p 15   SSA unac 1:10 E;   Bank
   Canzonette d'Amore (Kleine Lieder der Liebe), in MoTO X,
      p 3   SSA unac 1:00x3 E-M;   in Canzonetten . . . Bä 1562,
      p 5
   Canzonetten für drei geleiche Stimmen, edited by Hilmar Trede
      (see individual titles for complete information);   Bä 1562
         Canzonette d'Amore / Che vuol veder / La fiera vista / Il
         mio martir / Qual si può dir maggiore / Quando sperai del
         mio / Raggi dov'è'l mio bene / Son questi i crespi crini /
         Su su su che'l giorno / Tu ridi sempre mai.
   Canzonetten für gleiche Stimmen, edited by Hilmar Trede (see
      individual titles for complete information);   Bä 1754
         Chi vuol veder un bosco / Come farò cuor mio / Corse a la
         morte / Già mi credev' / Giù li a qual petto giace / Godi
         pur del bel / Io mi vivea / Io son fenice / Si come crescon
         alla terra / Vita de l'alma mia cara.
   Chi vuol veder d'invern'un dolce aprile (Wer will zur Winters-
      zeit den Maien sehen), in MoTO X, p 17   SSA unac 1:00x4
      M;   in Canzonetten . . . Bä 1562, p 16
   Chi vuol veder un bosco (Wollt sehen ihr des Waldes dicht
      Gezweige?), in MoTO X, p 23   SSA unac 1:00x4 E-M;   in
      Canzonetten . . . Bä 1754, p 18
   Come farò cuor mio quando me parto (Was soll ich tun mein
      Herz), in MoTO X, p 14   SSA unac 0:30x3 E-M;   in
      Canzonetten . . . Bä 1754, p 6
   Corse a la morte il povero Narciso (Jäh in den Tod Narzissus
      eilt), in MoTO X, p 15   SSA unac 0:30x4 M;   in Canzo-
      netten . . . Bä 1754, p 7
   Le fiera vista e'l velonoso sguardo (Grimme Gestalt und giftig),
      in MoTO X, p 4   SSA unac 1:30x4 E-M;   in Canzonetten
      . . . Bä 1562, p 6

Già mi credev' un sol ester in Cielo (Leuchtet die Sonn' allein strahlend am Himmel?), in MoTO X, p 18   SSA unac 0:45x4 E;   in Canzonetten . . . Bä 1754, p 8

Giù li a quel petto giace (An deiner Brust), in MoTO X, p 20 SSA unac 1:00x4 E;   in Canzonetten . . . Bä 1754, p 12

Godi pur del bel (Freue dich, sell'ger Floh), in MoTO X, p 19 SSA unac 0:45x4 E;   in Canzonetten . . . Bä 1754, p 10

Hodie Christus natus est, in MoTO XIV, p 26   SSA unac 1:25 M;   w/Monteverdi: Angelus, in MCD 24

Il mio martir (Verborgnes Leid), in MoTO X, p 9   SSA unac 2:00x3 E;   in Canzonetten . . . Bä 1562, p 10

Io mi vivea com' Aquila mirando (Frei wie des Adlers Flug), in MoTO X, p 11   SSA unac 0:30x3 E;   in Canzonetten . . . Bä 1754, p 5

Io son fenice e voi sete la fiamma (Phönix bin ich und du bist die Flamme), in MoTO X, p 22   SSA unac 1:00x3 E-M; in Canzonetten . . . Bä 1754, p 16

O Domine Jesu Christe adoro te in cruce pendetum [prima pars, see immediately below for secunda pars], in MoTO XIV, p 29 SSA unac 1:15 E;   Bank

O Domine Jesu Christe adoro te in cruce vulnertum [secunda pars, see immediately above for prima pars], in MoTO XIV, p 31   SSA unac 1:00 E;   Bank

Qual si può dir maggiore, in MoTO X, p 2   SSA unac 2:00 E; It Ger (Wie rein und lieblich bist du), in Canzonetten . . . Bä 1562, p 4;   It Ger (Wer sehen will zwei Bronnen), in Eur, p 5

Quando sperai del mio (Auf deine Huld), in MoTO X, p 13 SSA unac 1:00x4 E-M;   in Canzonetten . . . Bä 1562, p 14

Raggi dov'è'l mio bene, in MoTO X, p 6   SSA unac 1:15x2 E-M;   It Ger (Musik, du edle Gabe), in Eur, p 7;   It Ger (Kleine Lieder der Liebe), in Canzonetten . . . Bä 1562, p 5

Salve Regina, in MoTO XV, p 736   SS Bc 4:00 D;   ed HC-L, Bc realization by Vincent d'Indy, ES 1006

Si come crescon alla terra, in MoTO X, p 21   SSA unac 1:00x4 E;   It Ger (Wie Blumen spriessen aus der Erd), in Canzonetten . . . Bä 1754, p 14;   ed Herbert Zipper, trans Roger Maren, Eng only (As from the earth a flower grows), AJ 45

Son questi i crespi crini (Macht es dein lokkig Haar), in MoTO
   X, p 10   SSA unac 1:00x4 E-M;   in Canzonetten . . . Bä
   1562, p 12

Surgens Jesu, in MoTO XIV, p 46   SSA unac 1:15 M;   Bank

Su su su che'l giorno (Auf, auf, auf, der Tag will kommen), in
   MoTO X, p 12   SSA unac 1:00x4 E;   in Canzonetten . . .
   Bä 1562, p 13

Tu ridi sempre mai (Dein Lachen, holde Schöne), in MoTO X,
   p 16   SSA unac 1:00x2 E;   in Canzonetten . . . Bä 1562,
   p 15

Vita de l'alma mia cara (Leben du meiner Seel'), in MoTO X,
   p 8   SSA unac 1:00x3 M;   in Canzonetten . . . Bä 1754, p 4

MOORE, DOUGLAS 1893–

   Mary's wedding prayer, fr The devil and Daniel Webster—Now
   may there be a blessing   T: Stephen Vincent Benét   SSA,
   S solo, unac 1:20 M;   BoHa 5413

   Perhaps to dream—Now the day burns away   T: Stephen
   Vincent Benét   SSA unac 2:15 M;   CF CM 5242

MORALES, CRISTOBAL DE c. 1500–1553

   Agnus Dei   SSA unac 2:30 M;   ed Leo Kraft, Mercury MC
   359

MORLEY, THOMAS 1557–1603

   Cruel you pull away too soon, in EMS I, pt 1, p 9   SSA unac
   2:00 E-M

   Fire and lightning from heaven, in EMS, pt 1, p 19   SS unac
   0:30x2 D

   Flora wilt thou torment me, in EMS I, pt 1, p 20   SS unac
   0:45 0:15x2 E-M;   SB M 1a/8

   Good morrow, fair ladies, in EMS I, pt 2, p 27   SSA unac
   1:00 0:40x2 E;   SB M 1b/6;   N Octavo 565

   Go ye my canzonets, in EMS I, pt 1, p 1   SS unac 0:45 0:30x2;
   in Da, p 48;   SB M 1a/1

   Ho who comes here?, in EMS II, p 84   SSA unac 2:30 M;
   SB M 2/18;   Eng Ger (Frisch auf, ihr Musici), in Eur, p 43

   I go before my darling, in EMS I, pt 1, p 8   SS unac 1:15 E-M;
   SB M 1a/4;   I go before my charmer, ed GWW, ES 824

I should for grief and anguish, in EMS, pt 1, p 26   SS unac 0:45x2 M

In nets of golden wires, in EMS I, pt 1, p 22   ST(A) unac 0:35 0:10x2 E-M; SB M 1a/10

Lady, those eyes, in EMS I, pt 2, p 6 T: Sir John Davies, 1570–1626   SSA unac 1:10 E-M; SB M 1b/4

Leave now mine eyes lamenting, in EMS I, pt 1, p 17   SS unac 0:20 0:25x2 E-M; SB M 1a/7

Der Lenz all Äst bekleiden tut [w/original text: Spring-time mantleth every bough, in EMS I, pt 2, p 113]   SSA unac 0:30x2 E-M; Ger only, in JöW, p 38

Lo, here another love, in EMS I, pt 1, p 14   SS unac 1:15 E-M; SB M 1a/6

Love learns by laughing, in EMS I, pt 2, p 107   SSA unac 0:12x2 0:18x2 E-M; SB M 1/21

Miraculous love's wounding, in EMS I, pt 1, p 11   SS unac 1:40 E-M; SB M 1a/5

My heart why hast thou taken, in EMS II, p 117   SSSA unac 1:15x2 M

O sleep, fond fancy, not in EMS   SSA unac 1:00 E-M; in Da, p 60; SB M 1/25

O thou that art so cruel, in EMS I, pt 1, p 24   ST(A) unac 0:30 0:20x2 E-M; SB M 1a/11

Say, dear, will you not have me, in EMS I, pt 2, p 97   SSA unac 0:40 0:15x2 E

See, mine own sweet jewel, in EMS I, pt 2, p 1   SSA unac 0:50 E; SB M 1b/1

Spring-time mantleth every bough, see Der Lenz

Sweet nymph, come to thy lover, in EMS I, pt 1, p 6   SS unac 0:15x2 0:20x2; SB M 1a/3

This love is but a wanton fit, in EMS I, pt 2, p 109   SSA unac 0:10x2 0:15x2 E; SB M 1/22

Though Philomela lost her love, in EMS I, pt 2, p 111   SSA unac 0:35x2 E; SB M 1/23; ed Forsblad, Marks 4217

Thyrsis, let pity move thee, in EMS I, pt 2, p 61   SSA unac 1:15 E-M

Warum nicht lustig [w/original text: What ails my darling?, in EMS I, pt 2, p 29]   SSA unac 1:30 E-M; Ger only, in JöW, p 114

What ails my darling?, in EMS I, pt 2, p 29   SSA unac 1:30
E-M;   see Warum nicht lustig?

When, lo, by break of morning, in EMS I, pt 1, p 3   SS unac
2:00 E-M;   SB M 1a/2

Where art thou, wanton, in EMS I, pt 2, p 87   SSA unac 1:15
E-M

Whither away so fast?, in EMS I, pt 2, p 32   SSA unac 2:00
E-M;   SB M 1b/7

MOZART, WOLFGANG AMADEUS 1756–1791 Timings and grades are
not normally given as each piece may be considered 1–2 minutes
and E or E-M

Alleluja [canon] [K. 553], in MGA VII, no 52   four eq unac;
in Tov, p 50

Ave Maria [canon] [K. 554], in MGA VII, no 53   four eq unac;
in Tov, p 50

Difficile lectu (The watchman's cry) [canon] [K. 559], in MGA
VII, no 58   T: adapted Albert G. Latham fr Herrick   3 eq;
Eng only, in Whit, p 7

Kyrie [canon] [K. 89], in MGA III, no 2   five eq 5:00 M;   in
Tov, p 51

MUL, JAN 1910–

Laudate Dominum [1944]   T: Ps CXVII   SSA unac 1:00
M;   Bank

NANINI (NANINO), GIOV. MARIA 1545–1607

Laetamini in Domino   SSA unac 0:40 E-M;   Bank

NELSON, RON 1927–

He came here for me—Born in a stable   T: Ron Nelson
SSAA harp (pf) 3:00 E;   BoHa 5371

NEWARK, WILLIAM late 15th C

The farther I go   T: John Lydgate, 1370?–1451   SA unac
1:45 E-M;   SB Fayrfax 8

NICOLAUS PRAEPOSITUS DE PERUGIA c. 1360–c. 1375

Passando con pensier   TTT (SSS or SII) unac 5:00 M;   in
MET, p 16

NIN, JOAQUIN 1883–1949
   (And the angels woke the shepherds), fr Four Spanish folk songs
   —Eixa nit es nit de vetlla ('Tis tonight the night of vigil)   T:
   trans Elaine de Sinçay   SSAA pf 2:15 E-M;   Catalan Eng,
   Max Eschig (obtain through AM)
   Four Spanish folk songs (see individual titles for complete in-
   formation);   each published separately, Max Eschig (obtain
   through AM)
      (Neath an oak tree) / (And the angel woke) / (O my love) /
      (The girl who cares no longer).
   (Neath an oak tree), fr Four Spanish folk songs—Yo me iba
   madre (Mother, I was going)   T: trans Elaine de Sinçay
   SSAAdiv pf 1:00 E-M;   Spanish Eng, Max Eschig (obtain
   through AM)
   (O my love), fr Four Spanish folk songs—Meu amor (O my
   love)   T: trans Elaine de Sinçay   SSAA pf 2:15 E-M;
   Galician Eng, Max Eschig (obtain through AM)
   (The girl who cares no longer), fr Four Spanish folksongs—
   Fuistí a la siega y golviesti (From the harvest home returning)
   T: trans Elaine de Sinçay   SSAA pf 2:15 E-M;   Asturian
   Eng, Max Eschig (obtain through AM)

NORRIS, THOMAS 1741–1790
   Halleluja, hallelujah, amen [canon]   SSAA unac 0:25x2
   E-M;   ed Holst w/Webbe: I will, Webbe: From everlasting, Woodward: Let, in SB Part song 68
   I said I will take heed unto my ways [canon]   SSAA unac
   1:15 E-M;   w/Anon.:   Young, Webbe: Glory, Hayes: Alleluia, in SB Part song 85

NOWAK, LIONEL 1911–
   Wisdom exalteth her children   T: Eccl. IV: 11–12   SSASSA
   unac 3:15 E-M;   BCS 2

OBRECHT, JACOB 1450–1505
   Agnus Dei, fr Missa Beata viscera   SA unac 1:00 E-M;   in
   JöG, p 109

Missa sine nomine   SSA unac Ky 1:45 Gl 4:00 Cr 4:00 Sa
3:40 Be 4:10 Ag 5:45 M;   in Ste, p 71
Parce Domine   SSA unac 1:30 E-M;   Bank
Qui cum Patre [canon], fr Missa Salve diva parens   2 eq unac
1:00 M;   in Ste, p 26

OCKEGHEM, JOHANNES 1430–1495
Ma maîtresse [virelai]   SAA(II) unac 2:15 M;   in HAM I,
p 78

OLDROYD, GEORGE 1886–1951
As Joseph was a-walking   SSAA unac 3:00 M;   BoHa 1431

OTHMAYR, KASPAR 1515–1553
Ach das die Hilf aus Zion über Israel käme   T: Ps XVI: 7
TT (SS) unac 1:00 E-M;   in Geistliche, Bä 1933
Ach Gott, vom Himmel sieh darein   T: Martin Luther, Ps
XI   SA unac 0:50x4 E;   in Geistliche, Bä 1933
Auf dich, Herr, trau ich   T: Ps VII: 1   TT (SS) unac
0:30 E-M;   in Geistliche, Bä 1933
Aus tiefer Not schrei ich zu dir   T: Martin Luther, Ps CXXX
SA unac 1:00x5 E-M;   in Geistliche, Bä 1933
Christ lag in Todesbanden   T: Martin Luther   2 eq unac
0:45x3 E;   in Geistliche, Bä 1933
Durch Adams Fall ist ganz verderbt   T: Lazarus Spengler
SA (transposition necessary) unac 0:40x3 E;   in Geistliche,
Bä 1933
Erbarm dich mein, O Herre Gott   T: Erhart Hegenwalt, Ps
LI   SA unac 0:40x4 E-M;   in Geistliche, Bä 1933
Erhör mich, wenn ich rufe   T: Ps IV: 1   SA (transposi-
tion necessary) unac 1:00 E-M;   in Geistliche, Bä 1933
Es ist ein Schnee gefallen   SSAA unac 1:00 E;   in Eur, p 70
Ein feste Burg ist unser Gott   T: Martin Luther, Ps XLVI
SA unac 0:10x2 0:25 E-M;   in Geistliche, Bä 1933
Geistliche Zwiegesänge 1547. Bicinia sacra (see individual first
lines for complete information);   ed Walther Lipphardt, Bä
1933
Herr Christ der einig Gotts Sohn / Nun komm, der Heiden
Heiland / Gelobet seist du, Jesu Christ / Vom Himmel

hoch / Vom Himmel kam / Der Tag, der ist so freudenreich / Mit Fried und Freud ich fahr dahin / Christ lag in
Todesbanden / Komm, heiliger Geist / Nun bitten wir den
heiligen Geist / Nun freut euch, lieben Christen gmein
[two settings] / Nun freut euch / Mitten wir im Leben
sind / Durch Adams Fall / Vater unser im Himmelreich /
Gott sei gelobet / Ach Gott, vom Himmel / Ein feste Burg /
Erbarm dich mein / So wöll uns Gott genädig sein / Wär
Gott nit bei uns diese Zeit / Wo Gott der Herr nit bei uns
hält / Wo Gott zum Haus / Wohl dem, der in Gottes
Furcht steht / Aus tiefer Not / Ach dass die Hilf aus Zion /
Ich freue mich / Der Herr kennet den Weg / Auf dich,
Herr, trau ich / Steh auf, Herr, in deinem Zorn / Gott ist
ein rechter Richter / Erhör mich, wenn ich rufe.

Gelobet seist du, Jesu Christ   T: Martin Luther   SA (transposition necessary) unac 0:30 E;   in Geistliche, Bä 1933

Gott ist ein rechter Richter   T: Ps VII: 11–12   TT (SS)
unac 0:40 E-M;   in Geistliche, Bä 1933

Gott sei gelobet und gebenedeiet   SA unac 1:00 E;   in Geistliche, Bä 1933

Herr Christ der einig Gotts Sohn   2 eq unac 0:30 E;   in Geistliche, Bä 1933

Der Herr kennet den Weg der Gerechten   T: Ps I: 6   TT
(SS) unac 0:40 E;   in Geistliche, Bä 1933

Ich freue mich und bin fröhlich   T: Ps IX: 2   TT (SS)
unac 1:00 E-M;   in Geistliche, Bä 1933

Komm, heiliger Geist   T: Martin Luther   2 eq unac 1:00x3
E;   in Geistliche, Bä 1933

Mit Fried und Freud ich fahr dahin   SA unac 0:30x3 E;   in
Geistliche, Bä 1933

Mitten wir in Leben sind   T: Martin Luther   SA unac
0:50x3 E;   in Geistliche, Bä 1933

Nun bitten wir den heiligen Geist   SA unac 0:40 E;   in
Geistliche, Bä 1933

Nun freut euch lieben Christen gmein [1st setting]   T: Martin
Luther   SA unac 0:30x3 E;   in Geistliche, Bä 1933

Nun freut euch lieben Christen gmein [2d setting]   T: Martin
Luther   SI 0:30x3 E;   in Geistliche, Bä 1933

Nun komm, der Heiden Heiland   T: Martin Luther   SA
unac 0:30x4 E-M;   in Geistliche, Bä 1933
So wöll uns Gott genädig sein   T: Martin Luther, Ps LXVII
SA unac 1:00x3 E;   in Geistliche, Bä 1933
Steh auf Herr, in deinem Zorn   T: Ps VII: 6   SA unac
0:30 E-M;   in Geistliche, Bä 1933
Der Tag, der ist so freudenreich   SA unac 0:45x2 E-M;   in
Geistliche, Bä 1933
Vater unser im Himmelreich   T: Martin Luther   SA unac
1:00 E;   in Geistliche, Bä 1933;   Bä 264
Vom Himmel hoch   T: Martin Luther   2 eq unac 0:20x5 E;
in Geistliche, Bä 1933
Vom Himmel kam   T: Martin Luther   2 eq unac 0:20x3
E-M;   in Geistliche, Bä 1933
Wär Gott nit bei uns diese Zeit   T: Martin Luther, Ps CXXIV
SA (transposition necessary) unac 1:00x3 E;   in Geistliche,
Bä 1933
Wo Gott der Herr nit bei uns hält   T: Justus Joncs, Ps
CXXIV   SA unac 1:00x4 E;   in Geistliche, Bä 1933
Wo Gott zum Haus nit gibt sein Gunst   T: Johann Kolrose,
Ps CXXVII   SA unac 0:30x2 E;   in Geistliche, Bä 1933
Wohl dem, der in Gottes Furcht   T: Martin Luther, Ps
CXXVIII   SA unac 0:40x5 E;   in Geistliche, Bä 1933

OTT, JOHANN ?–1549?
Dies est laetitiae   SA unac 0:25 E;   in Ste, p 28
(In this our joyful holiday)   SA unac 0:40 E;   in Ste, p 28

PALESTRINA, GIOVANNI PIERLUIGI DA 1525–1594
Adoramus te, Christe, in PaW V, p 176   SSAA unac 1:15 E-M;
in Tov, p 40;   in Lei II, p 6;   JF 5281
Ah look upon these eyes, see Ahi che quest' occhi
Ahi che quest' occhi, in PaW XXVIII, p 135   SSA unac 0:20
E;   It Ger (Wie soll ich meiden dich), 2 vrs, in Eur, p 3;
Eng only (Ah look upon these eyes), 4 vrs, N MS 579;   Ger
only (Soll ich denn meiden dich), 3 vrs, in JöW, p 91
Alma redemptores Mater (Mary, our Savior's dear Mother)
[prima pars] Tu quae genuisti (Thou who hast begotten)

[secunda pars], in PaW V, p 156   SSAA unac 1:30 1:30 M-D;   in Da, p 72

Arbor decora, in PaW VIII, p 71   SSA unac 1:00 M;   ed Rossini w/Lassus: Eripe [arr?], in JF 6462

Assumpta est Maria in coelum [prima pars] Quae est ista [secunda pars], in PaW VI, p 28   SSAIII(TTB) unac or I 2:15 3:45 M;   MCD 1

Ave Maria, in PaW V, p 164   SSSA unac 2:30 D;   ed Damrosch, GS 6251

Ave Regina coelorum [prima pars] Gaude gloriosa [secunda pars], in PaW V, p 152   SSAA unac 2:15 2:15 M-D;   in Lei II, p 8;   ed Vauclain w/Pueri hebraeorum, in UPC 116

Benedictus, fr Missa Assumpta est, in PaW XXIII, p 115   SSAA unac 1:00 D;   in Lei II, p 16

Benedictus, fr Missa brevis, in PaW XII, p 60   SSA unac 1:30 M;   ed Bement, JF 7302

Benedictus, fr Missa Descendit angelus Domini, in PaW XX, p 17   SSA unac 1:15 M;   in Tov, p 14

Benedictus, fr Missa Lauda Sion, in PaW XIII, p 10   SSA unac 1:15 M;   in Tov, p 13;   in JöG, p 18;   in GM, p 120

Christe eleison, fr Missa Assumpta est Maria, in PaW XXIII, p 151   SSAA unac 1:10 M;   in PAG, p 3

Confitemini Domino, in PaW V, p 170   SSAA unac 1:10 M;   in Tov, p 42

Crucifixus, fr Missa Assumpta est, in PaW XXIII, p 109   SSAA unac 1:20 M;   in Lei II, p 13;   Lat Eng (Christ our Savior), GS 258

Crucifixus, fr Missa O Rex gloriae, in PaW XXI, p 30   SSA unac 1:15 M;   in Tov, p 21

Crucifixus, fr Missa Ut re mi, in PaW XII, p 176   SSAA unac 1:20 M-D;   in Lei II, p 18

(Crudelis Herodes) [original text: Lavacra puri gurgitis], in PaW VIII, p 20   T: fr hymn Hostis Herodes   SSA unac 1:00 M;   MR 2068

Esercizio sopra la scala (An exercise based on the scale)—(Ut, re, mi, fa), in PaW XXXI, p 99   SSAA unac 1:15 E;   text added, in Da, p 22

Gloria Patri (Praise to the Father), fr Magnificat tertii toni, in
PaW XXVII, p 14   SSAA unac 0:45 E-M; in RWOM,
ESV 869

Hodie Christus natus est, in PaW XXXI, p 135   SSAA unac
1:30 M; in Tov, p 48

Incipit lamentatio Jeremiae (Es erhebt sich das Klagelied Jeremiae), in PaW XXV, p 1   SSA 1:20 M-D; in JöG, p 105

Innocentes pro Christo, in PaW VII, p 66   SSAA unac 1:30
M-D; GS 5605

(Jesu dulcis memoria) [original text: Vates aeterni judicis], in
PaW VIII, p 94   T: fr hymn Christe redemptor omnium
SSA unac 1:00 M;   MR 2067

Jesu! Rex admirabilis, in PaW XXX, p 3   SSA unac 0:40x2
E; Lat Eng (Jesus trancendent), ed HC-L, ES 1074; in Tov,
p 22; Bank

Magnificat in the fourth mode, in PaW XXVII, p 244   SSAA
unac 6:30 D; MCD 24

O bone Jesu (O holy Father), in PaW XXXI, p 145   SSAA
unac 0:50 M; ed HC-L, ES 1812; ed EHG, GrayCMR 902;
Lat only, ed Taylor, JF 5053

Pleni sunt coeli [canon], fr Missa Sacerdotes Domini, in PaW
XVII, p 134   SSA unac 1:15 M-D; in JöG, p 138; in
Tov, p 16

Pleni sunt coeli (Himmel und Erde), fr Missa O magnum mys-
terium, in PaW XIII, p 131   SSA unac 1:00 M-D; in JöG,
p 139

Pueri Hebraeorum, in PaW V, p 172   SSAA unac 1:15 M;
in Ste, p 65; in Lei II, p 3; Lat Ger (Vieles Volk), in PAG,
p 5; ed Vauclain w/Ave Regina, in UPC 116

Salve Regina, in PaW V, p 160   SSAA unac 1:30 M-D; in
Tov, p 44; w/Lassus: Adoramus, Palestrina: Sub tuum,
in UPC 95

Soll ich denn meiden dich, see Ahi che quest' occhi

Sub tuum praesidium, in PaW V, p 173   SSAA unac 2:15
M-D; ed Taylor, JF 5051; w/Lassus: Adoramus, Palestrina: Salve Regina, in UPC 95

Tu nobis dona fontem lacrymarum, in PaW VIII, p 33   T: fr
hymn Ad preces nostras   SSA unac 1:20 M; MR 2013

Tua Jesu dilectio, in PaW XXX, p 4   SSA unac 0:30x2 E;
in Tov, p 23

Vide Domine (Siehe, Herr mein Gott), fr Lamentationum
Hieremiae Prophetae liber III, 1588, in PaW XXV, p 107
SSA unac 0:30 M;   in JöG, p 105

Wie soll ich meiden, see Ahi che quest' occhi

PATTISON, LEE 1890–
A babe is born   SSA unac Eng w/Lat, a macaronic 1:30 E;
GS Lawson-Gould 579

PEARSON, WILLIAM 1905–
From out of a wood did a cuckoo fly   SA, S solo unac 2:00 E;
Ox W 44

Sweet was the song the Virgin sang   T: 17th-C ballet   SSA
pf 2:40 E-M;   P Hinrichsen 58

PEETERS, FLOR 1903–
Ave Maria, gratia plena (Hail, Mary full of grace) [Op. 104d]
SA org 1:15 E;   P 6343

Missa in honorem Reginae pacis—Kyrie eleison   2 eq org Ky
2:10 Gl 3:00 Cr 4:30 Sa 1:15 Be 1:00 Ag 1:10 E-M;   MR 1692

PEPPING, ERNST 1901–
Ich armes Maidlein klag mich sehr   SSA unac 0:55x3 E-M;
Bä 2274

PERGOLESI, GIOVANNI BATTISTA 1710–1736
Fac, ut ardeat cor meum, fr Stabat Mater   SA 3:30 E-M;
string pts available, ES 1562;   in PAS, p 7

Quando corpus morietur, fr Stabat Mater   SA pf 2:30 M;
string pts available, ES 1527

Stabat Mater, fr Stabat Mater   SA pf 4:00 M;   in PAS, p 4;
in PAG, p 13;   MR 2343

Stabat Mater [complete]   SA, SA soli strings (pf) 3:30 2:50-S
aria 1:40 1:50-A aria 1:15-S aria 2:30-A aria 3:30 3:45 1:00-A
aria 2:00 2:30 M;   Lat Ger (Stand die Mutter), F minor, BH
60;   F minor, R 45422;   F minor, Kalmus;   E minor, each
section available separately, Lat Eng (Mother, bowed), Ox
46.100

Stabat Mater [excerpts]   SA strings (pf) 3:30 3:30 3:45 2:30
M;   Kalmus
    1. Stabat Mater / 8. Fac, ut ardeat cor meum / 9. Sancta
Mater / 12. Quando corpus.

Persichetti, Vincent 1915–
Hist whist [Op. 46, no 2]   T: E. E. Cummings   SA unac
1:10 E;   CF CM 6651
This is the garden [Op. 46, no 1]   T: E. E. Cummings   SSA
unac 2:30 M;   CF CM 6652

Peterkin, Norman 1886–
There is a lady sweet and kind   SA pf 2:00 E;   OxCS 2216

Petrejus, Johann ?–1550
Wer das Elend bauen will   SSA unac 0:35x2 E-M;   in JöW,
p 83
Wir sind bereit zur Winterzeit   SSA unac 1:40 E-M;   in
JöW, p 62

Petyrek, Felix 1892–1951
Drei frohe geistliche Lieder   T: fr Knaben Wunderhorn;   U
8325
    1. Weihnachtslied—Gott's Wunder lieber Bu'!   SSAA
       unac 3:15 M
    2. Ein Wahrheitslied—Als Gott der Herr geboren war
       SSAAdiv unac 5:45 M
    3. Jesukindleins Wiegenlied—Dormi, Jesu   SSAAdiv
       unac Lat 1:10 M

Phillips, Burrill 1907–
Bells, no 1 fr Declaratives—Oil and utilities   T: Tom Boggs
SSAA chamber orch (pf) 2:50 M;   Elkan-Vogel 3022
Declaratives (see individual titles for complete information)
    1. Bells / 2. Love / 3. Pueblos.
The hag   T: Robert Herrick   SSAA unac 2:00 M;   CF
CM 6486
Love, no 2 fr Declaratives—Love is more thicker than forget
   T: E. E. Cummings   SSAA chamber orch (pf) 5:00 M;
Elkan-Vogel 3023

Piggott, H. E.

Pueblos, no 3 fr Declaratives—Hi-y o-he, home for them
SSAA, SSAA soli chamber orch (pf) 3:00 M-D;   Elkan-Vogel
3024
What will love do—I bring you love   T: Robert Herrick
SSAA unac 3:00 M;   CF CM 6487

Piggott, H. E. 1878–
O sweet content—Art thou poor   T: Thomas Dekker, 1570–
1641?   SA pf 2:00 E;   OxCS T3

Pinkham, Daniel 1923–
Angelus ad pastores ait (Shepherds, awake)   SSAA, 3 trombones, tuba 2:30 E-M;   Music for Brass 614, Robert King
music co., North Easton, Mass.
Five canzonets   SA unac;   AM A–329
    1. The nut tree—I had a little nut tree   T: Old English
       nursery rhyme   0:45 E
    2. The blossom—Merry sparrow!   T: William Blake
       0:35 E-M
    3. Daybreak—Stay, O sweet, and do not rise!   T: John
       Donne, 1573–1631   1:00 E-M
    4. Calico pie—Calico pie, the little birds fly   T: Old
       English nursery rhyme   0:30 E-M
    5. Spring—Sound the flute   T: William Blake   0:15x3
       E

Playford, John 1623–1686
Comely swain   SSA unac 0:25x2 E;   ed Whittaker, w/Wil-
son: Where, in OxJP 28 and 29

Porpora, Niccola 1685–1767
Laetatus sum   SSAA, SA soli orch 7:00 M;   accompaniment
missing, UPC 26;   full score, ed Hans David, New York Public library publication;   cello part w/figured bass, Kalmus
Magnificat   SSAA, S solo orch 9:30 M;   accompaniment
missing, I pts available, UPC 8

Poulenc, Francis 1899–1963
Litanies à la Vierge Noire—Seigneur, ayez pitié de nous   SSA
org 2:00 M;   voice pts and score published separately, Durand

Petites voix   T: Madeleine Ley   SSA unac;   Rouart Lerolle
  1. La petite fille sage (The good little girl)—La petite fille
     sage (One day after school had closed)   1:15 E
  2. Le chien perdu (The lost dog)—Qui es-tu, inconnu?
     (Who are you, little dog) 0:55 E
  3. En rentrant de l'école (When coming home from school)
     0:30 E
  4. Le petit garçon malade (The little sick boy)—Le petit
     garçon malade (Oh the lonely little boy)   2:15 E
  5. Le hérisson (The hedge hog)—Quand papa trouve un
     hérisson (When Daddy found a young hedge hog)
     4:00 E

PRAETORIUS, MICHAEL 1571–1621
  Allein Gott in der Höh sei Ehr, fr Musae sioniae V, 1607, in
    PrW V, p 51   SA unac 1:00 M; in Zwiegesänge, p 47,
    Bä 1929
  Aus tiefer Not schrei ich zu dir, fr Musae sioniae IX, 1610, in
    PrW IX, p 104   SSA unac 2:25 E-M; in JöG, p 97
  Bless Thou my soul, see Nu, lob mein Seel [two settings]
  Born is a Child in Bethlehem, see Puer natus in Bethlehem
    [three-part setting]
  Christ fuhr gen Himmel, fr Musae sioniae IX, 1610, in PrW IX,
    p 59   AT (SA) unac 1:40 E-M; in Zwiegesänge, p 38, Bä
    1929
  Christ ist erstanden, fr Musae sioniae IX, 1610, in PrW IX, p 33
    SA unac 2:00 2:20 1:50 M; in Zwiegesänge, p 26, Bä 1929
  Christ lag in Todesbanden, fr Musae sioniae IX, 1610, in PrW
    IX, p 23   SA unac 3:00 M; in Zwiegesänge, p 31, Bä 1929
  Christ lag in Todesbanden, fr Musae sioniae IX, 1610, in PrW
    IX, p 22   SA unac 1:45 M; in JöG, p 33
  Christe, der du bist Tag und Licht, fr Musae sioniae IX, 1610,
    in PrW IX, p 16   AT (SA) unac 2:50 E; in Zwiegesänge,
    p 23, Bä 1929
  The clouds of night are passed away, see Surrexit Christus hodie
  Da Jesus an dem Kreuze stund, fr Musae sioniae IX, 1610, in

PrW IX, p 18   SA unac 1:40 E; in Zwiegesänge, p 25, Bä 1929

Dear Christians, one and all, see Nun freut euch

Ein Kind geborn zu Bethlehem, see Puer natus in Bethlehem [two-part setting]

Ein Kindelein so löbelich, fr Musae sioniae IX, 1610, in PrW IX, p 11   SS unac 3:20 M; in Zwiegesänge, p 12, Bä 1929

Erhalt uns Herr, see Veni redemptor gentium

Erstanden ist der heilig Christ, fr Musae sioniae IX, 1610, in PrW IX, p 31   AT (SA) unac 1:30 E; in Zwiegesänge, p 36, Bä 1929; see Surrexit Christus hodie for another setting

Es ist gewisslich an der Zeit, fr Musae sioniae IX, 1610, in PrW IX, p 147   SSA unac 0:15x4 0:15x2 E-M; in JöG, p 50

From heaven above to earth I come, see Vom Himmel hoch

Gelobet seist du, Jesu Christ, fr Musae sioniae IX, 1610, in PrW IX, p 4   SA unac 3:00 M; in Zwiegesänge, p 6, Bä 1929

Gott der Vater wohn uns bei, fr Musae sioniae IX, 1610, in PrW IX, p 71   AA unac 1:30 E-M; in Zwiegesänge, p 45, Bä 1929

How bright, how fair, see Wie schön leuchtet

Ich ruf' zu dir, Herr Jesu Christ (O Jesus, Lord of life and breath), fr Musae sioniae IX, 1610, in PrW IX, p 158   T: Greek Triodon "Sons of Syon"   SSA 1:30x2 M; Eng only, in Six settings, Con 97–7571

In Bethlehem ein Kindelein (In Bethlehem), fr Musae sioniae VI, 1609, in PrW VI, p 58—(It did be fall this winter's morn) SSAA unac 0:30x2 E; w/The fruitful seed of Jesse [SATB], Eng only, in SB Motets and Hymns 5

In dulci jubilo, fr Musae sioniae IX, 1610, in PrW IX, p 13 SA unac 1:30 M; Eng only (In dulci jubilo, sing we now, rejoicing), in Six Christmas, UPC 119; Ger Eng, CF 411; Ger only (In dulci jubilo, nun singet und seid froh), in Zwiegesänge, p 19, Bä 1929

In dulci jubilo, fr Musae sioniae V, 1607, in PrW V, p 162 SSA unac 2:00 M; in JöG, p 11; Eng only (In dulci jubilo, oh sing ye and rejoice), ed Gehrke, Con 98–1291

Jesus Christus, unser Heiland, fr Musae sioniae IX, 1610, in PrW IX, p 26   SS unac 1:40 M; in Zwiegesänge, p 34, Bä 1929

Komm, heiliger Geist, Herre Gott, fr Musae sioniae IX, 1610,
  in PrW IX, p 66   SSA unac 1:30 M-D;   in JöG, p 42
Komm, heiliger Geist, Herre Gott, fr Musae sioniae IX, 1610,
  in PrW IX, p 65   SA unac 2:00 M;   in Zwiegesänge, p 44,
  Bä 1929
Lord, keep us steadfast in Thy word, see Veni redemptor gentium
Nu, lob mein Seel (Bless Thou, my soul), fr Musae sioniae IX,
  1610, in PrW IX, p 134   SSA unac 1:50 E-M;   Eng only,
  in Six Christmas, UPC 119
Nu, lob mein Seel (Bless Thou, my soul), fr Musae sioniae IX,
  1610, in PrW IX, p 133   SS unac 2:40 E;   Eng only, in
  Six Christmas, UPC 119
Nun bitten wir den heiligen Geist, fr Musae sioniae IX, 1610,
  in PrW IX, p 64   TB (SA) unac 1:20 M;   in Zwiegesänge,
  p 42, Bä 1929
Nun freut euch (Dear Christians, one and all), fr Musae sioniae
  IX, 1610, in PrW IX, p 146   T: Martin Luther   SSA
  unac 1:25 M;   Eng only, in Six settings, Con 97–7571
Nun komm der Heyden Heiland, fr Musae sioniae IX, 1610, in
  PrW IX, p 1   SS unac 2:00 M;   in Zwiegesänge, p 4, Bä
  1929
Nun komm, der Heiden Heiland, fr Musae sioniae IX, 1610,
  in PrW IX, p 2   SSA unac 1:15 E-M;   in JöG, p 1
O Jesus, Lord of life and breath, see Ich ruf' zu dir Herr Jesu
  Christ
Oh, blest the house, see Wo Gott zum Haus
Our Father, thron'd in Heaven, see Vater unser
Puer natus in Bethlehem, fr Musae sioniae IX, 1610, in PrW
  IX, p 14   SA unac 1:15 E-M;   Lat Eng (Born is a child in
  Bethlehem), in Da, p 44;   Lat Ger (Ein Kind geborn), in
  Zwiegesänge, p 15, Bä 1929
Puer natus in Bethlehem (Born is a child in Bethlehem), fr
  Musae sioniae IX, 1610, in PrW IX, p 14   SSA unac 1:20
  E-M;   Eng only, in Six Christmas, UPC 119
Six Christmas chorales (see individual titles for complete infor-
  mation);   UPC 119
    In dulci jubilo / Puer natus in Bethlehem / Nu lob, mein

Seel [2 settings] / Wie schön leuchtet der Morgenstern / Wachet auf.

Six settings from "Musae sioniae, 1609" (see individual titles, Ger or Lat, for complete information); Con 97–7571
(From Heaven above to earth I come) Vom Himmel hoch / (Lord, keep us steadfast in Thy word) Veni Redemptor gentium / (Oh, blest the house) Wo Gott zum Haus / (Dear Christians, one and all, rejoice) Nun freut euch / (O Jesus, Lord of life and breath) Ich ruf' zu dir, Herr Jesu Christ / (The clouds of night are passed away) Surrexit Christus hodie.

Surrexit Christus hodie (The clouds of night are passed away) [based on Erstanden ist der heilige Christ], fr Musae sioniae IX, 1610, in PrW, p 33   T: Anon., 12th C   SSA 0:30x5 M;   Eng only, in Six settings, Con 97–7571

Der Tag, der ist so freudenreich, fr Musae sioniae IX, 1610, in PrW IX, p 9   SA unac 2:30 E-M;   in Zwiegesänge, p 10, Bä 1929

Vater unser in Himmelreich (Our Father, thron'd in Heaven high), fr Musae sioniae IX, 1610, in PrW IX, p 82   T: Martin Luther   SA unac 1:30 E;   ed Talmadge, ES 1967; Ger only, in HAM I, p 189

Veni redemptor gentium (Lord, keep us steadfast in Thy word), [based on Erhalt uns Herr], fr Musae sioniae IX, 1610, in PrW IX, p 214   T: Martin Luther   SSA unac 0:45x3 M; Eng only, in Six settings, Con 97–7571

Vom Himmel hoch, fr Musae sioniae IX, 1610, in PrW IX, p 6 TB (SA) unac 2:00 E;   in Zwiegesänge, p 8, Bä 1929

Vom Himmel hoch (From Heaven above to earth I come), fr Musae sioniae IX, 1610, in PrW IX, p 8   T: Martin Luther SSA unac 0:45x2 M;   Eng only, in Six settings, Con 97–7571

Wachet auf (Wake ye maids), fr Musae sioniae IX, 1610, in PrW IX, p 278   SA Bc optional 2:00 E;   Bc supplied separately, Eng only, in Six Christmas, UPC 119;   unac, Ger only, in Zwiegesänge, p 25, Bä 1929

Wake ye maids, see Wachet auf

Wenn mein Stündlein vorhanden ist, fr Musae sioniae IX, 1610, in PrW IX, p 234   SSA unac 1:15 E-M;   in JöG, p 52

Wie schön leuchtet der Morgenstern (How bright, how fair), fr
Musae sioniae IX, 1610, in PrW IX, p 273   SS Bc optional
1:20 E;   Bc supplied separately, Eng only, in Six Christmas,
UPC 119;   Ger only, w/2 vrs, in Zwiegesänge, p 17, Bä 1929
Wir danken dir, Herr Jesu Christ, fr Musae sioniae IX, 1610, in
PrW IX, p 61   SA unac 1:00x2 E;   in Zwiegesänge, p 40,
Bä 1929
Wo Gott zum Haus (Oh, blest the house), fr Musae sioniae IX,
1610, in PrW IX, p 151   T: von Pfeil   SSA unac 0:45x3
M;   Eng only, in Six settings, Con 97–7571
Zwiegesänge, (I) der Jahreskreis (see individual titles for complete information);   ed Gerhard Schwarz, Bä 1929
Nun komm der Heiden Heiland / Gelobet seist du, Jesu
Christ / Vom Himmel hoch / Der Tag der ist so freudenreich / Ein Kindelein so löbelich / Puer natus in Bethlehem / Wie schön leuchtet der Morgenstern / In dulci
jubilo / Wachet auf, ruft uns die Stimme / Christe, der du
bist Tag und Licht / Da Jesus an dem Kreuze stund / Christ
ist erstanden / Christ lag in Todesbanden / Jesus Christus,
unser Heiland / Erstanden ist der heilige Christ / Christ
fuhr gen Himmel / Wir danken dir, Herr Jesu Christ / Nun
bitten wir den heiligen Geist / Komm, heiliger Geist / Gott
der Vater wohn uns bei / Allein Gott in der Höh.

PURCELL, HENRY 1658–1695
I gave her cakes (Ich gab ihr Kuchen) [canon]   3 eq unac 1:30
M;   in GM, p 354
Sound the trumpet, in Purcell works XVIII, p 125   SA pf
0:40x2 0:45 M;   ES 487;   Au 4129b: Eng Dutch (Steekt de
trompetten), Musico (WLSM)

RATHBONE, GEORGE 1874–
Easter morning—At Easter as I went to praise   T: Irene Gass
3 eq unac 1:25 E;   N Trios 549

RAUCH, ANDREAS flourished c. 1600
Aller Augen warten auf dich   SSA unac 0:30 E;   in JöG, p 71
Ein Kellner und ein Koch   SSA unac 2:00 E-M;   in JöW,
p 129;   in Eur, p 87

RAVENSCROFT, THOMAS 1592–1640
   O Jesu meek   SSA org 2:00 E;   ESV 892

RAYNOR, JOHN 1909–
   An old lullaby—Hush, bonnie, dinna greet   T: Eugene Field,
      1850–1895   SA pf 1:45 E;   OxCS T50

READ, GARDNER 1913–
   Sisters, awake, close not your eyes [Op. 84, no 2a]   T: Thomas
      Bateson   SSA pf 1:30 E-M;   JF 8846

REDA, SIEGFRIED 1916–
   Ach, wie flüchtig   SA unac 1:00 M;   in Zwölf, Bä 1789
   Das alte Jahr vergangen ist   SA unac 0:45x5 E;   in Zwölf,
      Bä 1789
   Christum wir sollen loben schon   SA unac 0:45x4 E-M;   in
      Zwölf, Bä 1789
   Da Jesus an dem Kreuze stund   SA unac 0:30x9 E;   in Zwölf,
      Bä 1789
   Erhalt uns, Herr, bei deinem Wort   SA unac 0:30x3 E;   in
      Zwölf, Bä 1789
   Gelobet seist du, Jesu Christ   SA unac 0:30x7 E-M;   in
      Zwölf, Bä 1789
   Herr Gott, Vater im Himmelreich   SA unac 0:30x3 E-M;   in
      Zwölf, Bä 1789
   Jesus Christus, unser Heiland   SA unac 0:30x3 E-M;   in
      Zwölf, Bä 1789
   Komm, Gott Schöpfer, heiliger Geist   SA unac 0:45x7 E-M;
      in Zwölf, Bä 1789
   Nun komm, der Heiden Heiland   SA unac 0:30x5 E;   in
      Zwölf, Bä 1789
   O heilige Dreifaltigkeit   SA unac 0:30x5 E-M;   in Zwölf, Bä
      1789
   Wenn wir in höchsten Nöten sein   SA unac 0:30x7 E-M;   in
      Zwölf, Bä 1789
   Zwölf kanonische Choräle (see individual titles for complete
      information);   Bä 1789
         Ach, wie flüchtig / Christum wir sollen loben schon / Da
         Jesus an dem Kreuze stund / Das alte Jahr vergangen ist /

Erhalt uns, Herr, bei deinem Wort / Gelobet seist du, Jesu Christ / Herr Gott, Vater im Himmelreich / Jesus Christus, unser Heiland, der den Tod / Komm, Gott Schöpfer, Heiliger Geist / Nun komm der Heiden Heiland / O heilige Dreifaltigkeit / Wenn wir in höchsten Nöten sein.

REGER, MAX 1873–1916

Op. 79g, no 1 Lobt Gott, ihr Christen, allzugleich (Ye that have spent the silent night) [melody by Nikolaus Hermann] T: George Gascoigne   SSA unac 0:35x4 E; listed by publisher under Hermann, Eng only, GS 1504

Op. 111b Drei Gesänge T: trans Mrs. Bertram Shapleigh SSA unac; each published separately, BB

1. Im Himmelreich ein Haus steht (In Heaven doth a house rise) T: Spervogel, modern Ger by Will Vesper 1:30 E-M; BB

2. Abendgang im Lenz (Evening walk in spring)—Selig, selig durch die Fluren gehn (Silent, silent through the fields we go) T: L. Rafael 1:45 E-M; BB

3. Er ist's ('Tis spring)—Frühling lässt sein blauers Band (Springtime lets its azure band) T: Mörike 2:00 E-M; BB

Op. 111c Drei Gesänge [this is the same as Op. 111b, only arranged, presumably by Reger, for SSAA]; each published separately, BB

REGNART, JAKOB 1540–1599

Ach Gott, wie soll ich singen   SSA unac 0:20x6 E; in JöW, p 98

All mein Gedanken   SSA unac 0:15x6 E; in JöW, p 73; in Eur, p 60

Dies ist die Zeit, die mich erfreut   SSA unac 0:15x6 E; in JöW, p 96

Glaub nit, dass ich könnt sein   SSA unac 0:20x3 E; in JöW, p 95

Ich wollt, wer mir mein Glück nicht gönnt   SSA unac 0:20x8 E; in JöW, p 142

Ihrs Gleichen lebt auf Erden nicht   SSA unac 0:35x8 E; in Vier, P 4854

Mein Herz und Gmüt   SSA unac 0:30x8 E; in Vier, P 4854

Mein Mund, der singt   SSA unac 0:25x8 E; in JöW, p 10

Nach meiner Lieb viel hundert Knaben trachten   SSA unac
0:15x8 E; in JöW, p 99; in Vier, P 4854

Der süsse Schlaf   SSA unac 0:15x8 E; in JöW, p 30; in
Vier, P 4854

Venus, du und dein Kind   SSA unac 0:25x2 E; in GM, p 139

Vier Volksliedsätze (see individual titles for complete information); P 4854

    Der süsse Schlaf / Mein Herz und Gmüt / Nach meiner
    Lieb / Ihrs Gleichen lebt auf Erden nicht.

Wenn ich gedenk der Stund   SSA unac 1:00x3 E; in Eur,
p 58

Wer sehen will zween lebendige Brunnen   SSA unac 0:25x2
E; in GM, p 139

Rein, Walter 1893–1955

Herr, schicke, was du wilt (Lord, what Thou sendest me) T:
Mörike, trans Harvey Officer   SSA unac 2:30 M; Schott

Reinecke, Carl 1824–1910

(A Christmas carol) [Op. 163, no 9]—(When Christ was born)
T: H. C. Andersen   SA pf 3:00 E; GrayCMR 1558

(Look upward) [canon] T: Rückert 2 eq pf 2:30 E; ed
HC-L, trans John Troutbeck, ES 1937

Ten trios [Op. 100]   SSA pf

    1. Der träumende See (The dreaming lake)—Der See ruht
       tief (The lake lies rock'd) T: Julius Mosen 2:00
       E-M; N Trios 144

    2. Lob des Frühlings (Praise of spring)—Saatengrün,
       Veilchenduft (Fields of green, violet sheen) T: L.
       Uhland 3:00 E-M; N Trios 145

    3. Dein Sarg ist aus dem Stamm der Eichen (Of oak they
       mournful bier's prepared) T: Adolf Schults 1:40
       E; N Trios 146

    4. Sonnenblicke im Winter (Sunbeams in winter)—Was
       bringet mir den alten Muth (What calls my courage
       back to me) T: Justinus Kerner 2:30 E-M; N
       Trios 147

5. Der Morgen ist erwacht (The awaking of morn)—Es steigt am Himmel (Aloft in Heaven) T: Heinrich Stein 2:00 E-M; N Trios 148
6. Der Winter treibt keine Blüthe (The winter hath not a blossom) T: F. Bodenstedt 1:30 E-M; N Trios 149; Eng only, GS 203
7. Der selbst du mit dem Tode rangst (Thou that thyself with death hast striv'n) T: Friedrich Oser 1:00 M; N Trios 150
8. Der Abendwind (The evening wind)—Wie säuselt lind der Abendwind (How whispers kind the evening wind) T: Adolf Schults 1:00x2 0:15 E; N Trios 151
9. Wie auf dem Feld nur die Frucht gedeiht (As in the field goodly fruit will grow) T: F. Bodenstedt 1:30 E; N Trios 152
10. Elfe (The elves)—Bleib bei uns (Stay with us) T: Eichendorff 1:20 M; N Trios 153

RIEGGER, WALLINGFORD 1885–1961

Eternity—As if the sea should part T: Emily Dickinson SAdiv, SSAAA soli, flute, 2 horns, bass 2:15 M-chorus E-soli; I pts included, Flammer 83187

Evil shall not prevail—Wisdom is more beautiful than the sun T: Wisdom VII: 29–30 SSASSA (SSATTB) unac 6:50 E-M; BCS 3

ROGER-DUCASSE, JEAN JULES 1873–1954

Aux premières clartés de l'aube (At dawn of day), no 1 of Deux choeures—L'aube est calme (Day is dawning) T: Roger-Ducasse, trans Nita Cox SA(T) orch (pf) 5:30 M; pf score (Fr only), voice parts (Fr Eng), orch score, I parts, all available separately, Durand

Deux choeurs (see individual titles for complete information) Aux premières clartés de l'aube / Le joli jeu de furet.

Le joli jeu de furet (The pretty game of ferret), no 2 of Deux choeures—Au jeu! (To play) T: Roger-Ducasse, trans Nita Cox SA, S solo orch (pf) 7:00 M-D; pf score, voice parts, orch score, I parts, all available separately, Durand

ROGERS, BENJAMIN 1614–1698
In the merry month of May   T: Nicholas Breton   SSA
unac 1:00x2 E;   Jos. Williams St. Cecilia Series 17, no 20

ROREM, NED 1923–
A dirge—Rough wind, thou moanest loud   T: Shelley   SSA
unac 1:00 D;   in Five prayers, Presser 312–40307
Five prayers for the young [1953] (see individual titles for com-
plete information);   Presser 312–40307
A nursery darling / A dirge / Now I lay me down to sleep /
Fragment / The Virgin's cradle hymn.
Fragment: Wine and the fairies—I am drunk with the honey
wine   T: Shelley   SSA unac 0:40 D;   in Five prayers,
Presser, 312–40307
Now I lay me down to sleep   T: Shelley   SSA unac 1:00 D;
in Five prayers, Presser 312–40307
A nursery darling—A mother's breast: safe refuge from her
childish fears   T: Lewis Carroll   SSA unac 1:40 D;   in
Five prayers, Presser 312–40307
The Virgin's cradle hymn—Sleep, sweet babe   T: Coleridge
SSA unac 0:50 D;   in Five prayers, Presser 312–40307

ROSSI, LUIGI 1598–1653
Dormite, begl' occhi (So schlaf nun, ihr Augen)   SSA Bc 2:00
E-M;   in GM, p 248

ROSSINI, GIOACCHINO 1792–1868
La carità (La charité)—O caritade, virtù del cor (Force de l'âme,
O charité!)   T: Fr by Louise Colet   SSA, S solo pf 4:00
E-M;   R
La fede (La foi)—Alor che l'alma afflitta (Quand l'âme, aux
jours d'orage)   T: Fr by Goubaux   SSA pf 4:10 E-M;   R
La speranza (L'espérance)—Odi pietosa (Sainte espérance)   T:
Fr by Hyp. Lucas   SSA pf 4:30 M;   R

ROSTHIUS, NICOLAUS flourished c. 1600
Frau Nachtigal, mach dich bereit   SSAA unac 0:25x4 E;   in
JöW, p 20
Lieblich wohl kommt der Mai   SSAA unac 0:30x3 E;   in
JöW, p 35

ROUSSEL, ALBERT 1869–1937
Madrigal aux muses [Op. 25]—Souffrez les amours sur vos traces
    T: Gentil Bernard   SSA unac 3:30 M;   Durand

RUBBRA, EDMUND 1901–
The Virgin's cradle hymn—Dormi, Jesu! Mater ridet (Sleep, sweet babe!)   T: Eng by Coleridge   SSA unac 1:00 E; OxCS W24

SALAZAR, ADOLFO 1890–
Cuatro canciones sobre textos poetas españoles de los siglos XVI y XVII   SSA (no 3, SSA, SA soli) unac;   Max Eschig
    1. En el huerto nace la rosa   T: Gil Vicente   1:10 M
    2. Del rosal vengo, mi madre   T: Gil Vicente   1:35 E-M
    3. Muy graciosa es la doncella   T: Gil Vicente   2:00 E-M
    4. Bullicioso era el arroyuello   T: Anon.   1:00 E-M

SALINIS, HUBERTUS DE flourished c. 1420
Salve regina   SSA unac 3:00 M-D;   in GM, p 26

SANDERS, ROBERT L. 1906–
An American psalm [1945]—Great and marvellous is man's progress   T: fr Hymns of the spirit, Boston, 1937   SSA, flute, string quartet, bass, 2 pf (org) 15:00 D;   MP 107

SAN JUAN, PEDRO 1886–
Canto de cuna (Cradle song)—Arrorro mi nene (Hush my little child)   T: trans Pedro San Juan   SSA unac 3:30 M; Mercury, Merrymount
Lullaby   SSAASSAA, S solo unac textless [a vocalise] 4:30 E-M;   AJ 40

SANTA CRUZ, DOMINGO 1899–
Cantares de Pascua (Songs of Christmas) [Op. 27]   T: Santa Cruz   unac
    1. Del cielo salia Dios (From heaven the Lord came forth)
       SA 1:40 E;   Peer WO 510
    2. Llegó, llegó (He comes, He comes)   SA 0:50 E; Peer WO 511

3. El Niño Divino nace (The Son of God has been born)
T: Anon.   SSA 1:50 E;   Peer WO 512

4. Toquen arpas y guitarras (Play your harps)   T: Anon.
SSA 1:30 E-M;   Peer WO 513

5. Desde el fondo de mi alma (Deep within my soul's re-
cesses)   T: Anon.   SSA 2:10 E;   Peer WO 514

6. Alleluia, dies sanctificatus (Alleluia, a holy day)   T:
fr Christmas day mass   SSA 1:00 E-M;   Peer WO 515

7. Hodie Christus natus est (This day Christ is born)   T:
fr Christmas day mass   SSAA 2:30 E;   Peer WO 516

8. De los montes y los valles (From the hills and from the
vales)   SSAA 1:15 M;   Peer WO 517

9. Adoremos a Jesus (Let us adore Jesus)   SSAA 2:15 E;
Peer WO 518

10. Diálogo de Reyes (Dialogue of the kings)—Bajo el alero
frondoso de unas palmas centenarias (Under the shelter-
ing frondage of some centenary palmtrees)   SSASSA
4:30 M;   Peer WO 519

SARTORIUS, PAULUS before 1585?–?
Ich hab mir auserkoren   SSAA unac 0:15x6 E;   in Jö, p 73

SAYVE, LAMBERT DE 1549–1614
Warum willst du nicht fröhlich sein   SSSA unac 0:25 E-M;
in JöW, p 147

SCANDELLUS, ANTONIUS 1517–1580
Ach Gott, wem soll ich klagen?   SSAA unac 1:40 E-M;   in
JöW, p 108

SCHAERER, MELCHOIR before 1585–?
Ach Scheidens Art   SSA unac 0:55x3 M;   in JöW, p 89
So wünsch ich ihr ein gute Nacht   SSA unac 0:25x4 E-M;   in
JöW, p 26
Wer lützel hat und viel vertut   SSA unac 0:45x3 M;   in
JöW, p 155
Wie schön blüht uns der Maie   SSA unac 0:30x2 E-M;   in
JöW, p 42
Wo soll ich mich hinkehren   SSA unac 0:30x4 E-M;   in JöW,
p 157

SCHEIN, JOHANN HERMANN 1586–1630

    Christe, der du bist Tag und Licht   SS Bc 1:15x2 M;   in Sechs, p 3, Bä 1115

    Ein feste Burg ist unser Gott   T: Ps XLVI   SS Bc 1:15 M; in Sechs, p 13, Bä 1115

    Erschienen ist der herrliche Tag   SS Bc 2:00 M; in Sechs, p 16, Bä 1115

    Frau Nachtigall   SSA unac 0:50x2 E-M; in JöG, p 135

    Frohlocket nun, erhebet hoch   SSA unac 1:00x4 M; in JöG, p 40

    Gott der Vater wohn uns bei   SS Bc 2:00 M; in Sechs, p 20, Bä 1115

    Gott sei mir gnädig, see Herr, tu meine Lippen auf, and, Schaffe in mir

    Herr, tu meine Lippen auf, fr motet Gott sei mir gnädig   SSA unac 0:25 E; in JöG, p 83

    Ich ruf zu dir, Herr Jesu Christ   SS Bc 2:15 M; in Sechs, p 9, Bä 1115

    Kikeriki!   SSA unac 0:30x2 M; in JöW, p 19; Eng only (. . . is hen and rooster waking cry), 0:30x3, ed Woodside, W 2887

    Der kühle Maien   SSA unac 0:25x3 E; in JöW, p 45

    O schönestes Kindelein (O lovely Child)   SS org 0:30x2 0:30x2 E; Eng only, ES 2519

    Schaffe in mir, Gott, fr motet Gott sei mir gnädig   SSA unac 0:20 E; in JöG, p 83

    Sechs Choralkonzerte (see individual titles for complete information); Bä 1115

        Christe, der du bist Tag und Licht / Ein feste Burg / Erschienen ist der herrlich Tag / Gott der Vater wohn bei uns / Ich ruf zu dir / Vater unser im Himmelreich.

    Vater unser im Himmelreich   SS Bc 2:00 M; in Sechs, p 6, Bä 1115

    Viel schöner Blümelein   SSA unac 0:40x6 E; in JöW, p 46

SCHMITT, FLORENT 1870–1958

    Six choeures pour voix de femmes et orchestre [Op. 81]   SSAA orch (pf)

1. Le page et la reine—Un gentil page vint à passer   T: Paul Fort;   Durand 12117
2. Marionnettes—Pierrot, Guignol, Colombine   T: Charle-Auvrey;   Durand 12118
3. Si la lune rose   T: Cecile Sauvage;   Durand 12119
4. Ezann—Allah kébir!   T: Yks;   Durand 12120
5. L'amoureuse—Beaux yeux   T: Paul Fort;   Durand 12121
6. Canards liberaux—La tire dans l'eau   T: Aks;   Durand 12122

SCHRÖTER, LEONHART c. 1532–1595
Joseph, lieber Joseph mein   SSSA unac Ger and Lat [a macaronic] 1:10 M;   Ger and Lat, Ger-Ger, in JöG, p 8

SCHUBERT, FRANZ 1797–1828 Many of the compositions listed here were originally written for men's voices. In some cases, Schubert himself simply transposed them for women's voices.

Op. 11 [Deutsch 641, 724, 747], in SbW XVI, p 41   T: trans Henry S. Drinker   SSAA guitar? (pf?);   Eng only, Ger included but not underlaid in UPC editions
1. Das Dörfchen (The little village)—Ich rühme mir mein Dörfchen hier (My village fair)   T: G. A. Burger 3:40 E-M;   acc missing, UPC 51
2. Die Nachtigall (The nightingale)—Bescheiden verborgen (Away in the tree-tops)   T: Unger 6:30 E-M;   acc missing, UPC 52
3. Geist der Liebe—Der Abend schleiert Flur (The evening mist on field)   T: von Mattisson, 1761–1831 2:35 E-M;   acc missing, UPC 53

Op. 16 [Deutsch 740, 422], in SbW XVI, p 65   T: trans Henry S. Drinker   SSAA pf;   acc missing, Eng only, Ger included but not underlaid, UPC 54
1. Frühlingslied (Spring song)—Schmücket die Lokken (Gird ye with garlands)   T: Schober 3:15 E-M
2. Naturgenuss (Joy in nature)—Im Abendschimmer wallt der Quell (The brook flows on in evening light)   T: Matthisson 3:00 E-M

Op. 17 [Deutsch 983], in SbW XVI, p 138   T: trans Henry S. Drinker   SSAA unac;   Eng only, Ger included but not underlaid, UPC 55

   2. Liebe (Love)—Liebe rauscht der Silberbach (Love it is that stirs the brook)   T: Schiller, fr Der Triumph der Liebe   0:40x2 E-M

   4. Die Nacht (The night)—Wie schön bist du (How fair the night)   T: Krummacher?   2:30 E-M

Op. 52, no 4 Coronach [Deutsch 36], in SbW XVIII, p 1—Er ist uns geschieden vom Berg (He is gone on the mountain)   T: Walter Scott, fr Lady of the lake   SSA pf 2:30 E;   Ger only, in Frauen-Chöre, P 1047;   Eng only, N Trios 13

Op. 132 Psalm 23 [Deutsch 706], in SbW XVIII, p 3—Gott ist mein Hirt (The Lord is my shepherd)   SSAA pf 8:00 E-M;   Ger only, in Frauen-Chöre, P 1047;   Ger only, in PAG, p 16;   Ger only, in PAS, p 11;   ed Max Spicker, Eng only, GS 9110;   Eng only, D 3196;   Eng only, N Trios 67

Op. 133 Gott in der Natur [Deutsch 757], in SbW XVIII, p 10—Gross ist der Herr   T: Ewald Christian von Kleis [sometimes falsely attributed Gleim]   SSAA pf 5:40 E-M;   in PAS, p 16;   in PAG, p 21;   in Frauen-Chöre, P 1047;   Eng only (God in nature—Great is the Lord), trans Troutbeck, N Trios 15

Op. 134 Nachthelle [Deutsch 892], in SbW XVI, p 98—Die Nacht ist heiter (The night is clear)   SSAA, S solo pf 5:30 M;   Eng only, Ger included but not underlaid, acc missing, UPC 57

Op. 135 Ständchen [Deutsch 921], in SbW XVIII, p 20—Zögernd leise   T: Grillparzer   SSAA, A solo 5:30 M;   in Frauen-Chöre, P 1047;   Ger Eng (Serenade—Lingering softly), MCD 15;   trans Troutbeck, Eng only (Serenade—Creeping lightly), N Trios 16

Bekraenzet die Tonnen [Deutsch 427], in SbW XIX, p 73   T: Hölty   SSA unac 0:55x4 E;   in Zwei-, P 4639

Frauen-Chöre (see individual opus numbers or titles for complete information);   ed Dörffel, P 1047

   Op. 52, no 4 Coronach / Op. 132 Gott meine Zuversicht /

Op. 133 Gott in der Natur / Op. 135 Ständchen / Das grosse Hallelujah.

Gesang der Geister über den Wassern [Deutsch 538], in SbW XVI, p 175—Des Menschen Seele gleicht dem Wasser T: Goethe   SSAA unac 7:00 M; Ger Eng (The soul of man is like the water), UPC 56

Goldner Schein deckt den Hain [canon] [Deutsch 357], in SbW XIX, p 81 T: Matthisson 3 eq unac 2:40 E; in Zwei-, P 4639; Eng only (All the wold), T: trans Albert G. Latham, in Whit, p 10

Das grosse Hallelujah (Hallelujah) [as solo song, Deutsch 442], in SbW XX, Bd. IV, p 110—Ehre sei dem Hocherhab'nen (Glory unto God almighty) T: Friedrich Gottlieb Klopstock, 1724–1803   SSA pf 5:35 E-M; ed HC-L, ES 1041; Ger only, in Frauen-Chöre, P 1047; trans Troutbeck, Eng only, N Trios 17

Gruener wird die Au [Deutsch 199], in SbW XIX, p 91 [same melody and text set by Schubert for TBB (SAA), see below] T: Hölty   SA unac 0:20x3 E; in Zwei-, P 4639

Gruener wird die Au [Deutsch 129], in SbW XIX, p 72 [same melody and text set by Schubert as duet, see above] T: Hölty   SSA unac 0:30 E; in Zwei-, P 4639

Ein jugendlicher Maienschwung [canon] [Deutsch 61], in SbW XXI, p 333 T: Schiller 3 eq unac 1:45 E; in Zwei-, P 4639

Die Luft ist blau [Deutsch 243], in SbW XIX, p 75 T: falsely attributed to Hölty   SSA unac 0:45x2 E-M; in Zwei-, P 4639

Der Schnee zerrinnt [Deutsch 202], in SbW XIX, p 91 T: Hölty   SA unac 0:15x2 E; in Zwei-, P 4639

Sehnsucht [Deutsch 656], in SbW XVI, p 185—Nur wer die Sehnsucht kennt T: Goethe, fr Wilhelm Meister SSAAA unac 2:30 M; UPC 58

Unendliche Freude [canon] [Deutsch 54], in SbW XIX, p 78 T: Schiller 3 eq unac 2:40 E; in Zwei-, P 4639

Willkommen, lieber schöner Mai [canon] [Deutsch 244], in SbW XIX, p 85 T: Hölty 3 eq unac 1:10 E; in Zwei-, P 4639

Zwei- und dreistimmige Frauen- und Kinderchöre (see individ-
ual titles for complete information);   P 4639
  Gruener wird die Au / Der Schnee zerrinnt / Willkommen,
  lieber schöner Mai / Ein jugendlicher Maienschwung /
  Goldner Schein deckt den Hain / Unendliche Freude / Die
  Luft ist blau / Gruener wird die Au / Bekraenzet die
  Tonnen.

SCHULTZE, JOHANNES before 1585–1653
  Ich und du   SS unac 1:20x3 M-D;   in JöW, p 133

SCHUMAN, WILLIAM 1910–
  Beauty, fr Four rounds on famous words—All that glitters isn't
  gold   SSAA unac 2:15 E;   Presser 342–40007
  Caution, fr Four rounds on famous words—Look before you
  leap   SSAA unac 1:00 E-M;   Presser 342–40006
  Four rounds on famous words (see individual titles for complete
  information);   each published separately, Presser
    Health / Thrift / Beauty / Caution.
  Health, fr Four rounds on famous words—Early to bed and
  early to rise   SSAA unac 0:30 E;   Presser 342–40004
  Holiday song—When was it ever a waste of time   T: Gene-
  vieve Taggard   SSA pf 2:30 M;   GS 8948
  The Lord has a Child   T: Langston Hughes   SSA pf (org)
  2:40 D;   Presser 342–40008
  Prelude for women's voices—A stone, a leaf, an unfound door
  T: Thomas Wolfe, fr Look homeward, angel   SSAA, S
  solo, unac 5:50 M;   GS 8481
  Questions, fr This is our time—Never heard happier laughter
  T: Genevieve Taggard   SSAA flute, strings (pf) 6:50 M;
  BoHa 1656
  Requiescat—[textless]   SSAA pf 2:15 M;   GS 8928
  Thrift, fr Four rounds on famous words—He that goes aborrow-
  ing goes asorrowing   SSAA unac 1:30 E-M;   Presser 342–
  40005

SCHUMANN, ROBERT 1810–1856
  Frauenchöre von . . . mit Instrumentalbegleitung . . . von Hans

Pfitzner (see individual opus numbers for complete information);   U 2679

    Op. 69, no 3 Klosterfräulein / Op. 69, no 2 Waldmädchen / Op. 69, no 6 Die Kapelle / Op. 69, no 4 Soldatenbraut / Op. 91, no 2 Jäger Wohlgemuth / Op. 91, no 3 Der Wassermann / Op. 69, no 5 Merrfey / Op. 114, no 3 Spruch.

Gesänge für Frauenstimmen (see individual opus numbers for complete information);   ed Dörffel, P 2393

    Op. 69, no 1 Tamburinschlägerin / Op. 69, no 2 Waldmädchen / Op. 69, no 3 Klosterfräulein / Op. 69, no 4 Soldatenbraut / Op. 69, no 5 Merrfey / Op. 69, no 6 Die Capelle / Op. 91, no 1 Rosmarien / Op. 91, no 2 Jäger Wohlgemuth / Op. 91, no 3 Der Wassermann / Op. 91, no 4 Das verlassene Mägdlein / Op. 91, no 5 Der Bleicherin Nachtlied / Op. 91, no 6 In Meeres Mitten / Op. 114, no 1 Nänie / Op. 114, no 2 Triolett / Op. 114, no 3 Spruch / Op. 29, no 2 Lied.

Op. 29 Drei Gedichte von Emanual Geibel, in SmW Series X, vol II, p 2ff

    2. In meinem Garten die Nelken   T: Emanuel Geibel   SSA pf 3:10 E-M;   trans KKD, Ger Eng (Carnations grew in my garden), ES 1999;   in Gesänge, P 2393

Op. 69 Romanzen für Frauenstimmen, in SmW Series X, vol II, p 16ff

    1. Tamburinschlägerin—Schwirrend, Tamburin   T: fr Spanish by Eichendorff   SSAA pf ad lib. 0:25x3 E-M;   in Gesänge, P 2393;   trans W. G. Rothery, Eng only (Whirring tambourine), N Trios 384

    2. Waldmädchen—Bin ein Feuer hell   T: Eichendorff   SSAA soli pf ad lib. 1:05 M;   in Gesänge, P 2393;   w/orch by Pfitzner, in Frauenchöre, U 2679

    3. Klosterfräulein—Ich armes Klosterfräulein!   T: J. Kerner   SSAA pf ad lib. 1:00x3 E-M;   in Gesänge, P 2393;   w/orch by Pfitzner, in Frauenchöre, U 2679

    4. Soldatenbraut—Ach, wenn's nur der König auch wüsst   T: Mörike   SSAA pf ad lib. 1:15 M;   in Gesänge, P 2393;   w/orch by Pfitzner, in Frauenchöre, U 2679

5. Meerfey—Still bei Nacht T: Eichendorff   SSSAA
soli pf ad lib. 1:45 M-D; in Gesänge, P 2393; w/orch
by Pfitzner, in Frauenchöre, U 2679

6. Die Capelle [double canon]—Droben stehet die Capelle
T: L. Uhland   SSAA pf ad lib. 2:30 M-D; in
Gesänge, P 2393; w/orch by Pfitzner, in Frauenchöre,
U 2679

Op. 91 Romanzen für Frauenstimme, in SmW Series X, vol II,
p 32 ff

1. Rosmarien—Es wollt' die Jungfrau früh aufsteh'n
SSAA pf ad lib. 0:20x3 E-M; in Gesänge, P 2393

2. Jäger Wohlgemuth—Es jagt ein Jäger T: fr Knaben
Wunderhorn   SSAA pf ad lib. 0:20x4 E; in Gesänge,
P 2393; w/orch by Pfitzner, in Frauenchöre, U 2679;
Eng only (The merry huntsman—With blithesome heart
a huntsman bold), GS 154

3. Der Wassermann—Es war in des Maien mildem Glanz
T: J. Kerner   SSAA pf ad lib. 2:50 M; in Gesänge,
P 2393; w/orch by Pfitzner, in Frauenchöre, U 2679;
trans Rothery, Eng only (The river-king—May-beams
through the hawthorn's glance), N Trios 392

4. Das verlassene Mägdlein—Früh wann die Hähne kräh'n
T: Mörike   SSAA pf ad lib. 1:00 E-M; in Gesänge,
P 2393

5. Der Bleicherin Nachtlied—Bleiche, bleiche, weissen
Lein T: R. Reinick   SSAA pf ad lib. 0:30x4 E-M;
in Gesänge, P 2393

6. In Meeres Mitten T: Rückert   SSSAAA pf ad lib.
0:20x2 0:40 M; in Gesänge, P 2393

Op. 114 Drei Lieder, in SmW Series X, vol II, p 118ff

1. Nänie—Unter den rothen Blumen schlummere T: L.
Bechstein   SSA pf 0:50x3 E-M; in Gesänge, P 2393

2. Triolett—Senkt die Nacht T: C. L'egru   SSA pf
1:30 M; in Gesänge, P 2393; trans Troutbeck, Eng
only (Sinks the night), N Trios 165

3. Spruch—O blicke, wenn den Sinn T: F. Rückert
SSA pf 2:10 E-M; in Gesänge, P 2393; w/orch by
Pfitzner, in Frauenchöre, U 2679

117

SCHÜTZ, HEINRICH 1585–1672

Anima mea liquefacta est (Ach, meine Seele, schmilzt in Wonne hin) [prima pars] Adjuro vos, filiae Jerusalem (Ich flehe euch an, Töchter von Jerusalem) [secunda pars] [SWV 263], in ScW V, p 35   two eq, 2 high I, Bc 4:20 3:45 M;   ed Gerber, Bä 34

Auf dem Gebirge hat man ein Geschrei gehört [SWV 396], in ScW VIII, p 177   T: Matthew II: 18   AA, 2 gambas, 3 cellos 4:15 M;   ed Kamlah, Bä 528

Das Blut Jesu Christi [SWV 298], in ScW VI, p 36   T: I John I: 7   SSB Bc 2:00 M;   SSA, bass transposed up octave, Bc missing, in JöG, p 28

Bone Jesu, verbum patris [SWV 313], in ScW VI, p 107   T: after Manuale Divi Augustini XXXIX: 6–8; XVIII: 2 two eq Bc 6:00 M;   ed Ehmann and Soenke, w/Verbum, in Bä 3435

Eins bitte ich vom Herren [SWV 294], in ScW, p 29   T: Ps XXVII: 4   two eq Bc 2:30 M;   ed Hoffmann, w/O hilf, Meister, in Bä 1089;   in Zehn, p 21;   ed Leupold, Ger Eng (One thing have I desired), Con 98–1369

Erhöre mich, wenn ich rufe [SWV 289], in ScW VI, p 18   T: Ps IV: 2;   Ps V: 3   two eq Bc 1:45 M;   Ger Eng (Give ear, O Lord), MCD 13;   in Zehn, p 52;   ed Hoffmann w/Der Herr, O lieber, Habe deine, in Bä 1138

Die Furcht des Herren [SWV 318], in ScW VI, p 120   T: Ps CXI: 10   SA Bc 2:00 M;   in Zehn, p 26

Habe deine Lust an dem Herrn [SWV 311], in ScW VI, p 100   T: Ps XXXVII: 4–5   two eq Bc 5:30 M;   in Zehn, p 30;   ed Hoffmann w/Der Herr, O lieber, Erhöre, in Bä 1138

Herr, ich hoffe darauf [SWV 312], in ScW VI, p 105   T: Ps XIII: 6   two eq Bc 3:45 M;   in Zehn, p 44;   ed Ehmann and Koch, w/Ihr Heiligen, Lobet, in Bä 1704

Der Herr ist gross [SWV 286], in ScW VI, p 11   T: Ps CXLV: 3–4   two eq Bc 2:30 M;   Ger Eng (Great is our Lord), MCD 17;   in Zehn, p 16;   ed Hoffmann w/O lieber, Erhöre, Habe deine, in Bä 1138

Der Herr ist mein Licht und mein Heil [SWV 359], in ScW VII, p 110   T: Ps XXVII: 1, 6   two eq, 2 I 4:30 M;   I missing, in Zehn, p 10;   ed Hoffmann, Bä NMA 102

Heute ist Christus der Herr geboren (Jesus, our Savior, for us was born) [SWV 439], in ScW XIV, p 101   SSA Bc 6:10 M; ed Gore, Con 98–1570

Ich hab mein Sach, see Ich weiss, dass mein Herr Jesus Christ

Ich ruf zu dir [SWV 326], in ScW VI, p 144   SSB Bc 2:00 M; SSA, bass transposed up octave, Bc missing, in JöG, p 102

(Ich weiss, dass mein Herr Jesus Christ) [Original text: Jesu Christe, Jesu Christe, Gottes Sohn, fr Ich hab mein Sach] SSATB Bc [SWV 305] verse 17, for SSB, in ScW VI, p 85   SSB Bc 1:30 M;   SSA, bass transposed up octave, Bc missing, 1:30x2, in JöG, p 27

Ihr Heiligen, lobsinget dem Herren [SWV 288], in ScW VI, p 116 T: Ps XXX: 5–6 two eq Bc 2:45 M; ed Herrmann, Eng Ger (Sing, O ye saints), Con 98–1414; ed Ehmann and Koch w/Lobet, Herr ich hoffe, in Bä 1740; in Zehn, p 5

Jesu Christe, Jesu Christe, Gottes Sohn, see Ich weiss, dass mein Herr Jesus Christ

Lobet den Herren, der zu Zion wohnet [SWV 293], in ScW VI, p 27 T: Ps IX: 11–12   AA Bc 1:30 M; ed Ehmann and Koch w/Ihr Heiligen, Herr ich hofe, in Bä 1704

Meister, wir haben die ganze Nacht gearbeitet [SWV 317], in ScW VI, p 119 T: Luke V: 5 two eq Bc 1:15 M; ed Hoffmann w/Eins bitte, O hilf, in Bä 1089

O hilf, Christe, Gottes Sohn [SWV 295], in ScW VI, p 30 two eq Bc 2:00 M; in Zehn, p 48; ed Hoffmann w/Ein bitte, Meister, in Bä 1089

O lieber Herre Gott [SWV 287], in ScW VI, p 13 T: Martin Luther 2 eq Bc 3:10 M; Ger Eng (Oh mighty God, our Lord), MCD 18; ed Agey, Ger Eng (O gracious Lord God), Con 98–1558; ed Hoffmann w/Der Herr, Erhöre mich, in Bä 1138

Veni, rogo, in cor meum (Come, I pray Thee, dwell within me) [SWV 83], in ScW IV, p 115 T: Manuale Diva Augustini XXXIII: 5   SSAA unac 4:30 D; ed EHG, lowest voice sometimes transposed, GS 8981

Verbum caro factum est [SWV 314], in ScW VI, p 111 T: John I: 14 two eq Bc 3:30 M; ed Ehmann and Soenke w/Bone, in Bä 3435

Was betrübst du dich, meine Seele [SWV 253], in ScW VII, p 69
T: Ps XLII: 11 two eq, 2 I, Bc 4:45 M; Ger Eng (Why
afflict thyself, O my spirit), MCD 20; 2 I missing, in Zehn,
p 35

Wie ein Rubin in feinem Golde leuchtet [SWV 357], in ScW
VII, p 98 T: Ecclesiasticus (Sirach) XXXII: 7–9 two eq,
2 I, Bc 2:30 M; Bä 1086

Zehn geistliche Duette (see individual titles for complete infor-
mation); ed Dittberner, C. F. Kahnt
Ihr Heiligen, lobsinget dem Herren / Der Herr ist mein
Licht und mein Heil / Der Herr ist gross und sehr löblich /
Eins bitte ich vom Herren / Die Furcht des Herren / Habe
deine Lust an dem Herren / Was betruebst du dich, meine
Seele / Herr, ich hoffe darauf / O hilf, Christe, Gottes Sohn
/ Erhöre mich, wenn ich rufe.

SENFL, LUDWIG c. 1490–1542 or 1543

Ego ipse consolabor vos (I am, myself, the one that comforteth
you) T: Isaiah LI: 12–13, 15 SA unac 1:20 M; in Da,
p 40

SERMISY, CLAUDE DE c. 1490–1562

Auprès de vous (To be near you) SA unac 2:00 M; ed
David, w/Certon: Je n'ose, Je suis, Jacotin: Je suis, in MP
34

SHAKE, J. CURTIS 1918–

A Christmas carol—Jesus the saviour was born today T:
Shake SSA unac 1:45 E; JF 9261

SHEPHERD, ARTHUR 1880–1958

Carol—Make we merry both more and lasse SA pf 0:15
1:00x3 E-M; w/Jolly Wat, in MP 106

Jolly Wat—What shall I sing but Hoy! T: Balliol Ms., 15th–
16th C SA pf (org or orch) 2:20 E-M; w/Carol, in MP
106

SHEPPERD, JOHN c. 1520–c. 1563

Gloria in excelsis—Hodie nobis caelorum rex (Heute ist der
himmlischen König) SSAA unac 3:00 M; in Das Chorwerk LXXXIV, p 4, Möseler

SLAVENSKI, JOSIP 1896–1955
Vöglein spricht (Ftiček veli da se ženil bude) [1924]—Spricht das Vöglein (Ftiček veli)   SSAA pf 5:00 M;   Schott

SMITH, LEO 1921–
Carol [1947]—Christ and Mary led me on a footstool   T: St. Godric   SSA unac 1:00 E-M;   AJ 10
Christmas carol [1943]—I sing of a maiden   SA unac 1:15 M-D;   Peer

SMITH, RUSSELL 20th C
Set me as a seal   T: Solomon VIII: 6   SSA unac or horn and string trio 2:30 M-D;   I pt available fr publisher, GS Robert Shaw 589

SOWERBY, LEO 1895–
O Jesus, Thou the beauty art   T: St. Bernard of Clairvaux, trans Edward Caswall, 1849   SSA unac 3:00 E-M;   Gray-CM 1508

SPEEDING, FRANK 1929–
The morning chase—The hunt is up   T: Shakespeare   SA pf 2:30 E;   OxCS T30

SPELMAN, TIMOTHY MATHER 1891–
Her litany of waiting, a cantata—Hasten, beloved, your coming!   T: Leolyn Louise Everett   SSA, S solo orch;   Ch

SPITTA, HEINRICH 1902–
Ich wollt, dass ich daheime wär   T: Heinrich von Laufenberg, 15th C   SSA unac 4:00 M;   in JöG, p 60
Weihnachtliche Liedkantata (Christmas cantata)—Vom Himmel hoch, ihr Englein kommt (From heaven above, ye angels all)   SSA, S solo, Vio I, Vio II, Bc 7:00 E-M;   Ger only, score, part book, I pts, all available separately, Möseler; Trans Anna Hoppe, Eng only, Con 97–7597 (score), Con 97–6355 (violins), Con 97–6356 (cello)

STADEN, JOHANN 1581–1634
Danket dem Herren   SSA unac 1:20 E;   in JöG, p 73
(The eyes of all wait upon Thee) T: Ps CXLV: 15–16   SSA unac 0:55 E;   Con 98–1326

STEUCCIUS, HEINRICH

Herr, unser Herrscher T: Ps VIII   SSA unac 3:00 E-M;
in JöG, p 130
Ein jeder Mensch bedenke eben   SSA unac 1:00 E-M; in
JöG, p 49
Lobet den Herren, alle heiden T: Ps CXVII   SSA unac
1:00 M; in JöG, p 129
(Oh, praise the Lord, all ye nations) T: Ps CXVII   SSA
unac 1:15 E-M; Con 98–1327
Vater unser, der du bist   SSA unac 1:20 E; in JöG, p 76
Zion spricht: Der Herr hat mich verlassen   SSA unac 1:45
E-M; in JöG, p 126

STEUCCIUS, HEINRICH c. 1585–?
Herzliebstes Liebelein   SSAA unac 0:45x8 E-M; in JöW,
p 78
Zwölftausend Mägdelein   SSAA unac 0:35x4 E-M; in JöW,
p 143

STRATEGIER, HERMAN 1912–
Ecce Virgo   SSAA unac 1:45 M; Dutch included, not underlaid, Bank

STRAVINSKY, IGOR 1882–
Cantata—This ae nighte T: Anon. 15th, 16th C   SSAA,
ST soli, 2 flutes, oboe, english horn (oboe), cello 30:00 M;
miniature score, BoHa 17245; vocal score, BoHa 17247
(Four Russian peasant songs) (Vier russische Bauernlieder);
Eng Fr, AJ 27; Russian Ger, Schott
    1. (On Saints' days in Chigisakh) (Près de l'Église à Chigi-
    sak) (Beim Heiland von Tschigissi)   SSAA unac 1:00
    M-D
    2. (Ovsen) (Ovsen) (Herbst)   SA unac 0:35 M-D
    3. (The pike) (Le brochet) (Der Hecht)   SSAA, SAA soli
    unac 1:00 M-D
    4. (Master Portly) (Monsieur Ventru) (Freund Dicksack)
    SSAA unac 1:15 D

SWEELINCK, JEAN PIETERSZOON 1562–1621 In SwW VIII, Rimes
françoises et italiennes, there are ten or more pieces, depending
upon the range of the altos, suitable for women's voices not listed
below.

Beaux yeux, par qui l'Amour [prima pars] Voila comm'en
l'esprit [secunda pars], in SwW VIII, p 9   SA unac 2:00
2:00 M;   Senart 2895

Io mi son giovinetta (I am a damosel), in SwW VIII, p 22   SA
unac 2:15 M;   in Da, p 45

Je pars, non point de vous [prima pars] Mais pourtant ma
douleur [secunda pars], in SwW VIII, p 4   SA unac 1:30
1:30 E-M;   Senart 2894

Las! que me sert [prima pars] L'enfant Amour [secunda pars],
in SwW VIII, p 1   SA unac 1:40 1:40 M;   Senart 2899

Lorsque le trait [prima pars] Brief, mon esprit [secunda pars],
in SwW VIII, p 6   SA unac 1:45 1:45 M;   Senart 2896

Marchans qui traversez [prima pars] Voyez le filets [secunda
pars], in SwW VIII, p 16   SA unac 2:00 2:00 M;   Senart
2898

Voici du gai printemps [prima pars] Le Dieu Mars [secunda
pars], in SwW VIII, p 12   SA unac 2:00 2:00 M;   Fr Eng
(Behold the happy time) (Two Gods, Mars and sweet love), in
Da, p 49;   Senart 2897

TALLIS, THOMAS c. 1505–1585
Sancte Deus   SSAA unac 3:30 M;   in Ste, p 45

TAVERNER, JOHN c. 1495–1545
Audivi   SSAA unac 1:20 M;   in Ste, p 30
Gloria in excelsis   SSAA unac 2:30 M;   in Ste, p 33

THIMAN, ERIC 1900–
A shepherd kept sheep [canon]   SS pf 1:05 E;   N Choral
songs 111

THOMAS, CHRISTOPHER 1894–
Elfin song—Ouphe and goblin! imp and sprite!   T: Joseph
Rodman Drake   SSA unac 1:30 M;   B. F. Wood 532
The house and the road—The little road says, go   T: Jo-
sephine Preston Peabody   SSAA pf 0:45 M;   B. F. Wood
493

THOMAS, KURT 1904–
Wenn ich mit Menschen- und mit Engelzungen redete [Op. 25,
no 18]   SA, baritone solo unac 3:00 M;   BH 3518

123

THOMPSON, RANDALL 1899–
 Come in, fr Frostiana—As I came to the edge of the woods   T: Robert Frost   SSA pf 4:30 E;   ES 2539
 The gate of heaven—I was glad   T: Psalm CXXII: 1; Habakkuk II: 20; Genesis XXVIII: 17   SSAA unac 4:30 M;   ES 2531
 A girl's garden, fr Frostiana—A neighbor of mine   T: Robert Frost   SSA pf 2:50 E;   ES 2540
 Now I lay me down to sleep   T: New England primer   SSA unac 1:30 E;   ES 1985
 Pueri Hebraeorum   SSAASSAA unac 2:10 E;   ES 492
 Rosemary   T: Stephen Vincent Benét;   ES 1023
   1. Chemical analysis—She's slender hands and pretty lips SSA unac 2:10 E-M
   2. A sad song—Rosemary, there's a pig in your garden SSAA unac 2:10 E-M
   3. A nonsense song—Rosemary, let down your hair   SSA unac 3:00 E-M
   4. To Rosemary—Not where the sober sisters   SSAA unac 6:00 M

THOMSON, VIRGIL 1896–
 Agnus Dei [canon]   3 eq unac 2:10 E-M;   Mercury M 153
 Behold how good and pleasant it is   T: Ps CXXXIII unison unac 1:10 M-D; w/Unto Thee, and, O give, in Three antiphonal psalms, Leeds L 253
 Medea of Euripides, seven choruses   T: Countee Cullen SSAAdiv, SAA soli, unac, percussion ad lib.;   Mercury
   1. O gentle heart   1:10 D
   2. Love, like a leaf   1:10 D
   3. O, happy were our fathers   1:20 M-D
   4. Weep for the little lambs   0:40 M-D
   5. Go down, O sun   0:30 D
   6. Behold, O earth   1:30 D
   7. Immortal Zeus controls the fate of man   1:10 M-D
 O, give thanks to the Lord   T: Ps CXXXVI   SSAA unac 2:25 M-D; w/Unto, Behold, in Three antiphonal psalms, Leeds L 253

Unto Thee lift I up mine eyes   T: Ps CXXIII   SA unac
1:00 M-D;   w/Behold, O give, in Three antiphonal psalms,
Leeds L 253

TOCH, ERNST 1887–
 The lamb—Little lamb, who made thee?   T: William Blake
 SSdivA unac 1:20 D;   Mills 665 (Affiliated)

TOMKINS, THOMAS 1573–1656
 Fond men, that do so highly prize, in EMS XVIII, p 14   SSA
 unac 1:10 E-M;   SB M 18/4
 Love, cease tormenting, in EMS XVIII, p 24   SSA unac 1:00
 0:20x2 E-M;   SB M 18/6
 Sure there is no god of love, in EMS XVIII, p 10   SSA unac
 0:50 0:25x2 M;   SB M 18/3

TSCHESNOKOFF, see CHESNOKOFF

TURNHOUT, GERARD c. 1520–1580
 En regardant par une traille (Jüngst shaut' ich bass)   SA unac
 2:00x2 E-M;   in GM, p 134

VAET, JAKOB ?–1567
 Sicut cervus   SA unac 4:00 E;   Bank

VAN HULSE, see HULSE

VAN KOERT, HAN 1913–
 This is our accepted time [based on tune of Vulpius]   T:
 Michael Gannon   3 eq unac 1:00 E-M;   WLSM

VAUGHAN WILLIAMS, RALPH 1872–1958
 Dirge for Fidele—Fear no more the heat   T: Shakespeare
 SSA unac 4:30 E;   BoHa 5385
 Land of our birth, fr Thanksgiving for victory   T: Kipling
 SSA orch (pf) 3:15 E;   Ox 54.900
 Magnificat—Hail, thou that art highly favoured   SSAA, A
 solo orch (flute and pf) 11:30 E-M;   Ox 46.200
 O taste and see   T: Ps XXXIV: 8   SA, S solo org 1:15
 E-M;   Ox 82.003

Riders to the sea—Where is she?   T: J. M. Synge   SSAA,
baritone soli, SSAA orch (pf) 30:00 M [this work is mostly
solo writing];   vocal score, Ox 56.520, choral parts 56.510

The shepherds of the delectable mountains (Die Hirten der
lieblichen Berge)—Who so dwelleth (Wer lebet)   T: fr
Bunyan's Pilgrim's progress   3 men soli, S solo, SSASSA orch
17:30 [including chorus 1:30] M;   full score, Ox 56.009, vocal
score, Ox 56.315, chorus part, Ox 56.320

Sigh no more, ladies, fr In Windsor forest   T: Shakespeare
SSA, A solo ad lib. orch (pf) 2:45 E-M;   Ox 54.143

Willow-wood, a cantata—I sat with love upon a woodside well
T: D. G. Rossetti   SSA, baritone solo orch (pf) 12:00
E-M;   BH

VECCHI, ORAZIO 1550–1605
Ist nicht einer vorhanden   SSA unac 0:15x4 E;   in JöW,
p 113

VENTO, IVO DE c. 1540–1575
Entlaubet ist der Walde   SSA unac 0:50 E-M;   in JöW, p 58
Gott ist mein Trost, hat mich erlöst   SSA unac 1:10 E-M;   in
JöG, p 31
Ob ich schon arm und elend bin   SSA unac 1:45 E-M;   in
JöW, p 145
Vater unser im Himmelreich   SSA unac 1:30 E-M;   in JöG,
p 81

VERDI, GIUSEPPE 1813–1901
Laude alla Vergine Maria, fr Quattro pezzi sacri—Vergine
madre, figlia del tuo Figlio   T: fr Dante's Paradise   SSAA
unac 5:30 M;   ed Kurt Soldan, P 4256c;   It Eng (Hymn to
the Virgin—O Virgin Mother), Ricordi 114157;   ed Zipper,
trans Harold Heiberg, Eng only (Praises to the Virgin Mary—
Thou Virgin Mother), AJ 8

VIADANA, L. G. DA 1564–1627
Hoc signum crucis   2 eq org 2:00 E;   MR 2352

VIERDANCK, JOHANN 17th C
Weihnachtskonzert (A Christmas concert)—Ich verkündige

euch grosse Freude (Lo, I bring unto you) T: Luke II:
10–12, 14   SS (SA) 2 melody I Bc 6:00 E;   trans and ed
Frances Alice Kleeman, each I part and score available
separately, Eng only, JF 9156;   ed Hans Engel, Ger only,
score and parts, Bä 468

VILLA-LOBOS, HEITOR 1881–1959
   Mass in honor of St. Sebastian   SSA unac Ky 3:15 Gl 6:30
      Cr 10:15 Sa 2:40 Be 2:45 Ag 2:15 M;   AM

VITTORIA, TOMÁS LUIS DE c. 1549–1611
   Accende lumen sensibus, in ViW V, p 35   T: fr Veni Creator
      Spiritus, Pentecost hymn   SSA unac 1:00 E-M;   in Tov,
      p 11
   Aegra currit, in ViW V, p 58   T: fr Lauda mater, Feast of
      St. Mary Magdalen hymn   SSA unac 1:00 E-M;   in Four-
      teen verses, UPC 110
   Arbor decora, in ViW V, p 23   T: Vexilla regis, Good Friday
      hymn   SSA unac 1:45 E-M;   in Fourteen verses, UPC 110
   Christe eleison, fr Missa Laetatus, in ViW VI, p 61   3 eq unac
      0:40 E;   in Tov, p 15
   Coeduntur gladiis, in ViW V, p 80   T: fr Sanctorum meritis,
      Feast of Martyrs hymn   SSA unac 1:30 E;   in Fourteen
      verses, UPC 110
   Consurgit Christus, in ViW V, p 29   T: fr Ad coenam Agni
      providi, Easter hymn   SSA unac 1:00 M;   in Fourteen
      verses, UPC 110;   same music as Divina cujus, see below
   Creator alme siderum [original text: Cujus forti potentiae], in
      ViW V, p 2   SSA unac 1:20 E-M;   MR 2305;   same music
      as Cujus forti, see below
   Cujus forti potentiae, in ViW V, p 2   T: fr Conditor (Creator)
      alme siderum, Advent hymn   SSA unac 1:20 E-M;   in
      Fourteen verses, UPC 110;   same music as Creator alme
      siderum, see above
   Divina cujus caritas [original text: Consurgit Christus], in
      ViW V, p 29   T: fr hymn Ad regias Agni dapes   SSA
      unac 1:00 M;   MR 2070;   same music as Consurgit Christus,
      see above

Duo Seraphim clamabant [prima pars] Tres sunt, qui testi-
monium dant [secunda pars], in ViW I, p 36   SSAA unac
1:45 1:45 M; in Tov, p 32; Lat Eng (Lo, two seraphim)
(Three there be), ed Schindler, D 13 381; Ger only (Musik,
schöner Klang) (Musik, du edle Kunst), in Eur, p 32, p 35

Fourteen verses from vesper hymns (see individual titles for
complete information); UPC 110

> Cujus forti / Sic praesens / Vos prima / Insere tuum / Ar-
> bor decora / Consurgit Christus / Verbum caro [2 settings] /
> Monstra te esse / Aegra currit / Martyres dei / Quorum
> praecepto / Coeduntur gladiis / Virgo singularis.

Insere tuum, in ViW V, p 19   T: fr Ad preces, Quadragesima
Sunday hymn   SSA unac 1:00 E-M; in Fourteen verses,
UPC 110; MR 2012

Judus Mercator, in ViW V, p 136   SSAA unac 1:30 E-M; in
Ste, p 61

Martyres Dei, in ViW V, p 68   T: fr Christe Redemptor
omnium, All Saints day hymn   SSA unac 1:00 E; in Fourteen verses, UPC 110

Monstra te esse, in ViW V, p 48   T: fr Ave maris stella, Office
of our Lady hymn   SSA unac 1:00 M; in Fourteen verses,
UPC 110

Musik, du edle Kunst, see Duo Seraphim clamabant [secunda
pars]

Musik, schöner Klang, see Duo Seraphim clamabant [prima
pars]

O Regem coeli [prima pars] Natus est nobis [secunda pars], in
ViW I, p 29   SSAA unac 2:00 2:00 M; in Lei III, p 3;
ES 2535

O sacrum convivium, in ViW I, p 34   SSSA unac 1:00 1:00
M; in Tov, p 36

O vos omnes, in ViW I, p 27   SSSA unac 2:40 E-M; in Tov,
p 30; Lat Ger (O ihr alle), in JöG, p 25; ESV 871; Bank

Quorum praecepto, in ViW V, p 71   T: fr Exultet coelum
laudibus, Feast of an Apostle hymn   SSA unac 1:30 E-M;
in Fourteen verses, UPC 110

Sic praesens, in ViW V, p 7   T: fr Christe Redemptor omnium, Christmas hymn   SSA unac 1:10 M; in Fourteen

verses, UPC 110; same music as Tu lumen et splendor, see below

Tu lumen et splendor [original text: Sic praesens testatur dies], in ViW V, p 7 T: fr hymn Jesu Redemptor omnium SSA unac 1:10 M; MR 2069; same music as Sic praesens, see above

Una hora, in ViW V, p 140 SSAA unac 0:30 0:30x2 E; in Ste, p 57

Verbum caro, in ViW V, p 41 T: fr Pange lingua gloriosi, Feast of Corpus Christi hymn SSA unac 1:20 E-M; in Fourteen verses, UPC 110

Verbum caro, in ViW V, p 97 T: fr Pange lingua gloriosi, Feast of Corpus Christi hymn SSA unac 1:45 E-M; in Fourteen verses, UPC 110

Virgo singularis, in ViW V, p 110 T: fr Ave maris stella, Office of Our Lady hymn SSA unac 0:30 E-M; in Fourteen verses, UPC 110

Vos prima Christi victima, in ViW V, p 9 T: fr Salvate, flores Martyrum, Feast of Holy Innocents hymn SSAA unac 2:00 E-M; in Fourteen verses, UPC 110

VON DOHNÁNYI, see DOHNÁNYI

VOYNICH, E. L. 1864–

I saw three ships SSAA, SSAA soli unac 1:40 E; GrayCMR 744

Our Lady sings SSAASSAA unac 2:45 E; in Ste, p 117

Three jolly shepherds—As I out rode this enderes night SSA unac 2:20 M; GrayCMR 742

WAGNER, RICHARD 1813–1883

(Spinning chorus), fr Flying Dutchman—(Good wheel be whirring) SSAA orch (pf) 15:00 M-D; Eng only, GS 187; Eng only, GS 336

WALKER, GEORGE 1922–

Gloria in memoriam—Gloria in excelsis Deo SSA, SSA soli org 2:15 D; New valley music press

WALTHER, JOHANN 1496–1570
  Jesus Christus, unser heiland   SSA unac 1:00 E; in JöG,
    p 39

WARD, JOHN before 1585?–before 1641
  Fly not so fast, in EMS XIX, p 26   SSA unac 0:25x2 0:25x2
    E-M; SB M 19/6
  Go, wailing accents, in EMS XIX, p 21   SSA unac 1:15 E-M;
    SB M 19/5
  His heart his wound received, in EMS XIX, p 7 T: Sir
    Philip Sidney, 1554–1586   SSA unac 1:00 0:20x2 E-M
  In health and ease am I, in EMS XIX, p 17 T: Francis
    Davison, c. 1575–c. 1619   SSA unac 1:00 E-M
  My true love hath my heart, in EMS XIX, p 1 T: Sir Philip
    Sidney, 1554–1586   SSA unac 1:30 M; SB M 19/1
  O say, dear life, in EMS XIX, p 12   SSA unac 1:40 E-M;
    SB M 19/3

WARLOCK, PETER, see PHILIP HESELTINE

WARNER, RICHARD 1908–
  The spruce tree carol—When Jesus lay on Mary's knee T:
    Katherine Root Warner   SSA pf (org) or harp and strings
    3:30 E; Summy-Birchard B 1612

WARRELL, ARTHUR S. 1882–
  Praise to the Lord T: Neander, trans Winkworth   SSAdiv,
    unison chorus, strings and org (pf) 3:00 E-M; SB Church
    music lib 472
  A safe stronghold T: Martin Luther, trans Thomas Carlyle
    SSA, unison chorus, strings and org (pf); SB Church music
    lib 375
  Sunset—No breath disturbs the fragrant ev'ning air T: B.
    Dunbar Dey   SSA unac 4:00 E; OxCS 531
  A triumph song—To God with heart T: George Wither
    SSA (SA), unison chorus, string, winds ad lib., org (pf) 3:00 E;
    SB Church music lib 496

WEBBE, SAMUEL 1740–1816
  From everlasting to everlasting Thou art God [canon] 3 eq

4

unac 1:00x2 0:15 E; w/Webbe: I will, Woodward: Let, Norris: Halleluja, in SB Part song 68

Glory be to the Father [canon] SSAA unac 1:40 E-M; w/Anon.: Young, Norris: I said, Hayes: Alleluia, in SB Part song 85

Hot cross buns [canon] 5 eq unac 1:30 E; in HAM II, p 275

I will magnify Thee O God [canon] 3 eq unac 0:30x2 0:10 M; w/Webbe: From everlasting, Woodward: Let, Norris: Halleluja, in SB Part song 68

Who can express the noble works of God? [canon] SSA unac 3:00 E; ed Holst, w/Boyce: Glory, Boyce: Alleluja, Anon.: As pants, in SB Part song 45

Would you know my Celia's charms? [canon] 4 eq unac 1:00 E; w/Byrd: Non, Byrd: Hey ho, in N SS 1895

WEELKES, THOMAS c. 1575–1623

The ape, the monkey and the baboon, in EMSXIII, p 24 SSA unac 0:20x2 E-M; SB M 13/10

Ay, me, my wonted joys, in EMS IX, p 22 SSSA unac 2:20 M

Come let's begin to revel't out, in EMS XIII, p 1 SSA unac 0:12x2 0:12x2 E; SB M 13/1

Come sirrah Jack ho, in EMS XIII, p 14 SSA unac 0:15x4 0:15x4 E-M; ESR 840; in Da, p 64

Donna il vostro bel viso, in EMS XIII, p 60 SSA unac 0:20x2 0:20x2 E-M

Four arms, two necks, one wreathing, in EMS XIII, p 35 SSA unac 0:15x3 0:20x3 E; ESR 834

The gods have heard my vows, in EMS XIII, p 20 SSA unac 0:35x3 E

Ha, ha, this world doth pass, in EMS XIII, p 47 SSA unac 0:35x3 E-M; in Da, p 62

I bei ligustri e rose, in EMS XIII, p 42 SSA unac 0:12 0:35x2 E-M

Jockie thine horn-pipe's dull, in EMS XIII, p 3 SSA unac 0:20x2 0:15x2 E; SB M 13/2

Late is my rash accounting, in EMS XIII, p 32 SSA unac 0:20x3 0:20x3 E-M; SB M 13/13

Lo, country sports, in EMS IX, p 58   SSAA unac 0:40 0:15x2
E-M;   SB M 9/12;   in Da, p 91

Lord, when I think, in EMS XIII, p 38   SSA unac 0:10x4
0:20x4 E-M

The nightingale, the organ of delight, in EMS XIII, p 62   SSA
unac 0:40 0:25x2 M;   SB 13/25;   in Da, p 66

No, though I shrink still, in EMS XIII, p 26   SSA unac
0:15x2 0:15x2 E;   SB M 13/11

Our country swains, in EMS IX, p 54   SSAA unac 0:35
0:35x2 M

Say, wanton, will you love me?, in EMS XIII, p 40   SSA unac
0:20x2 0:20x2 E;   SB 13/16

Some men desire spouses, in EMS XIII, p 6   SSA unac 0:20x4
0:20x4 E

Strike it up tabor, in EMS XIII, p 45   SSA unac 0:10x2
0:15x2 E;   SB M 13/18

Tan ta ra, cries Mars, in EMS XIII, p 17   SSA unac 0:15x2
0:25x2 E-M

Though my carriage be but careless, in EMS XIII, p 22   SSA
unac 0:15x2 0:10x2 E;   SB M 13/19

Tomorrow is the marriage day, in EMS XIII, p 9   SSA unac
0:10x6 0:15x6 E;   SB M 13/4

Upon a hill the bonny boy, in EMS XIII, p 11   SSA unac
0:20x4 0:20x4 E;   SB M 13/5

Weigel, Eugene 1910–

A cradle song—The angels are stooping above your bed   T:
W. B. Yeats   SSA unac 3:00 D;   in Four songs, New valley
music press

A drinking song—Wine comes in at the mouth   T: W. B.
Yeats   SSA unac 1:20 D;   in Four songs, New valley music
press

Four songs (see individual titles for complete information); New
valley music press
    To an isle in the water / A drinking song / A cradle song /
    To a squirrel at Kyle-na-no.

To a squirrel at Kyle-na-no—Come play with me   T: W. B.
Yeats   SSA unac 2:40 D;   in Four songs, New valley music
press

To an isle in the water—Shy one of my heart   T: W. B. Yeats
SSA unac 3:00 D;   in Four songs, New valley music press

WEISS, HELMUTH 1899–
Bittegesang—Heut gehn wir mit dem Kreuz   SSA unac 1:45
E;   in JöG, p 111

WHITE, L. J. 1910–
A prayer of St. Richard of Chichester—O holy Jesus, most merciful redeemer   SA pf (org) 1:45 E;   Ox E 43

WIDMANN, ERASMUS 1574–1634
Es ist ein edle Gottesgab   SSAA unac 2:00 E;   in Eur, p 77
Kommt her, ihr Herrn Studenten frei   SSAA unac 0:40x3
E-M;   in JöW, p 118
Wer Lust und Lieb zur Musik hat   SSAA unac 0:40 0:20x2
E-M;   in JöW, p 1
Wohlauf, ihr Gäste   SSAA unac 0:35x2 1:10x2 M;   in Eur,
p 72;   same music as Wohlauf, Soldatenblut, see below, in
JöW, p 125
Wohlauf, Soldatenblut   SSAA unac 0:35x2 1:10x2 M;   in
JöW, p 125;   same music as Wohlauf, ihr Gäste, see above, in
Eur, p 72

WILBYE, JOHN 1574–1638
Ah, cruel Amarillis, in EMS VII, p 12   SSA unac 2:30 E;
SB M 7/3
As fair as morn, in EMS VII, p 22   SSA unac 1:50 E-M;   SB
M 7/5;   in Da, p 68
Away thou shalt not love me, in EMS VI, p 10   SSA unac
1:40 2:20 E-M;   SB M 6/2
Ay, me, can every rumour?, in EMS VI, p 10   SSA unac 2:40
E-M
Come shepherd swains, in EMS VII, p 1   SSA unac 2:15 M;
ed Greenberg, AM NYPMA 2;   SB M 7/1
Dear pity, how? Ah how?, in EMS VI, p 19   SSA unac 1:45
E-M
Fly love aloft to heaven, in EMS VI, p 1   SSA unac 0:45
0:35x2 E-M;   SB M 6/1
O what shall I do?, in EMS VIII, p 27   SSA unac 2:15 M

So light is love, in EMS VII, p 17   SSA unac 1:10 0:45x2 E;
SB M 7/4

Weep O mine eyes, in EMS VI, p 15   SSA unac 3:00 E-M;
ed Greenberg, AM NYPMA 1

WILLAERT, ADRIAN between 1480/90–1562
Sur le ioly ioly ionc   SSA unac 3:00 M;   in MET, p 67

WILLAN, HEALEY 1880–
Tyrle, tyrlow—About the field they piped right   T: fr Balliol
Ms 1536   SSAA unac 2:10 E-M;   BM 1807

WILLIAMS, GRACE 1906–
Blow, blow, thou winter wind, fr Three lyrics from the plays of
Shakespeare   T: Shakespeare   SSA pf 1:20 E-M;
w/Sigh, Orpheus, in Ox 54.933

Orpheus with his lute, fr Three lyrics from the plays of Shakespeare   T: Shakespeare   SSAdiv pf 2:00 E-M;   w/Sigh,
Blow, in Ox 54.933

Sigh no more, ladies, fr Three lyrics from the plays of Shakespeare   T: Shakespeare   SSA pf 1:20 E-M;   w/Orpheus,
Blow, in Ox 54.933

WILLIAMS, JOHN GERRARD 1888–1947
An autumn picture—The feathers of the willow   T: R. W.
Dixon   SA pf 3:00 E;   OxCS 110

I loved a lass, a fair one   T: George Wither   SA pf 3:40 E;
OxCS 111

WILLIAMS, R. VAUGHAN, see VAUGHAN WILLIAMS

WILSON, JOHN 1595–1673 or 1674
Where the bee sucks   SSA unac 0:40 E-M;   ed Whittaker,
w/Playford: Comely, in OxJP 28 and 29

WINN, CYRIL 1884–
Forty-one descants to familiar hymn tunes;   Ox

WINSLOW, RICHARD 1918–
Against pride in clothes—How proud we are   T: Isaac Watts
SSAdiv pf 4:45 M;   GS Lawson-Gould 634

Huswifery—Make mee, O Lord, thy spinning wheele compleat
T: Edward Taylor   SSA pf 3:50 M;   CF CM 6587

WOODWARD, RICHARD 1744–1777
Let the words of my mouth [canon]   SSAA unac 0:30x2 E;
w/Webbe: I will, Webbe: From everlasting, Norris: Halleluja, in SB Part song 68

YOULL, HENRY 16th–17th C
Awake, sweet love, in EMS XXVIII, p 11   SSA unac 0:35
0:20x2 E; SB M 28/11
Come love, let's walk, in EMS XXVIII, p 5   SSA unac 0:50
0:35x2 E; SB M 28/2
Come, merry lads, let us away, in EMS XXVIII, p 91   SSA
unac 1:20 E; SB M 28/20
Each day of thine, in EMS XXVIII, p 1   SSA unac 0:50 E;
SB M 28/1
Early before the day doth spring, in EMS XXVIII, p 99   SSA
unac 0:40x2 0:40x2 E; SB M 28/22
In the merry month of May, in EMS XXVIII, p 91   SSA unac
0:40x2 E; SB M 28/19
In yonder dale, in EMS XXVIII, p 11   SSA unac 0:30 0:10x2
0:30 E-M; SB M 28/3
Only joy, now here you are, in EMS XXVIII, p 6 T: Sir
Philip Sidney, 1554–1586   SSA unac 0:35 0:30x2 E-M; SB
M 28/6
See where this nymph, in EMS XXVIII, p 16   SSA unac 0:50
0:20x2 E-M; SB M 28/4
Sweet Phyllis, stay, in EMS XXVIII, p 64   SSA unac 0:35x2
0:35 E; SB M 28/14

ZANGIUS, NICOLAUS ?–before 1620
Ducke dich, Hänsel   SSA unac 0:10x6 0:25x3 M; in JöW,
p 141
Mir gliebt im grünen Maien   SSA unac 0:10x6 0:10x3 0:15x6
E; in JöW, p 47

SECTION TWO

Collections

Bruder Singer. Chorausgabe für gleiche Stimmen. Edited by Richard Baum. Kassel and Basel: Bärenreiter-Verlag [Edition Bä 3881], 1961. This is a collection of 66 sacred and secular compositions, easy to medium-difficult, by modern composers. The pieces are for two to four women's voices, unaccompanied, with German or Latin texts only. The complete contents, given below, are not indexed under composer.

Koch: Ach bitterer Winter / Genzmer: All mein Gedanken / Bender: All Morgen ist ganz frisch / Knorr: Als ein behutsam Licht / Müntzel: Als wir jüngst in Reg'nsburg / Koch: Ännchen von Tharau / Götsch: Dort niedn in jenem Holze / Koch: Du mein einzig Licht / Rohwer: Einen Tanz mit der Königin / Götsch: Es, es, es und es / Marx: Es flog ein klein Waldvögelein / Kukuck: Es führt über den Main / Blumensaat: Es geht eine helle Flöte / Schwarz: Es ist ein Ros entsprungen / Bornefeld: Es ist ein Schnitter / Bender: Es kommt ein Schiff, geladen / Bialas: Es taget vor dem Walde / Watkinson: Es wollt ein Jägerlein jagen / Wolters: Freunde, lasst uns fröhlich loben / Koch: Die güldne Sonne / Watkinson: Hab mein Wage voll gelade / Neumeyer: Der hat vergeben / Müntzel: Heissa Kathreinerle / Thate: Die helle Sonn leucht jetzt / Watkinson: Heut soll das grosse Flachsernten sein / Marx: Hört, ihr Herrn / Watkinson: Ich bin der junge Hirtenknab / Genzmer: Ich fahr dahin / Luchterhandt: Ich wollt ein Bäumlein steigen / Knigge: Ich wollt, wenn's Kohlen schneit / Götsch: Im Frühtau zu Berge / Bornefeld: Ein Jäger aus Kurpfalz / Rein: Jauchzet Gott [canon] / Marx: Jeden Morgen geht die Sonne auf / Marx: Jetzt fängt das schöne Frühjahr an / Hensel: Jetzt geht es in die Welt / Marx: Jetzt kommt die fröhliche Sommerzeit / Müntzel: Kein Feuer, keine Kohle / Götsch: Kein schöner Land / Koch: Kommt, ihr Gspielen / Watkinson: Kuckuck ruft im Tannen-

wald / Götsch: Das Lieben bringt gross Freud /
Luchterhandt: Der Maien ist kommen / Koch:
Maria durch ein Dornwald / Wolters: Mich
brennt's in meinen Reiseschuhn / Götsch: Morgen-
sonne lächelt / Zipp: Muss i denn / Bornefeld:
Nach grüner Farb / Seifert: Nun ruhen alle Wälder
/ Dietrich: Nun singet und seid froh / Götsch:
O du schöner Rosengarten / Maasz: O Freude über
Freude / Maasz: Rosastock, Holderblüt / Lau:
Scheint die helle Sonne / Marx: Sine musica nulla
vita [canon] / Genzmer: So treiben wir den Winter
aus / Schwarz: Vom Himmel hoch, da komm /
Distler: Wach auf, du deutsches Land / Pepping:
Wach, Nachtigall, wach auf / Klein: Wenn ich ein
Vöglein wär / Lau: Wer sich die Musik erkiest /
Schwarz: Wieder einmal ausgeflogen / Köhler: Der
Wind, der Wind, der weht / Bornefeld: Wo Gott
zum Haus nicht gibt sein Gunst / Watkinson:
Wohlauf, ihr Wandersleut / Müntzel: Zum Tanze,
da geht ein Mädel.

Da David, Hans (ed). *The Art of polyphonic song. Compositions of the 16th and 17th centuries for two to
eight parts.* New York: G. Schirmer, 1940. The contents are indexed separately under composer.

Palestrina: Alma redemptoris mater / Wilbye: As
fair as morn / Lassus: Beatus homo / Weelkes:
Come, sirrah Jack, ho / Hassler: Core mio / Le
Jeune: Le courant des eaux / Senfl: Ego ipse con-
solabor vos / Palestrina: Esercizio sopra la scala /
Lassus: Exspectatio justorum / Morley: Go ye, my
canzonets / Weelkes: Ha ha, this world doth pass
/ Byrd: In crystal towers / Ferrabosco: In Thee,
O Lord / Sweelinck: Io mi son giovinetta /
Weelkes: Lo, country sports / Lecouteux (?):
Louange et gloire / Le Jeune: O Seigneur, j'espars
/ Morley: O sleep, fond fancy / Praetorius: Puer
natus in Bethlehem / Le Jeune: Quant la terre au
printemps / Lassus: Qui sequitur me / Weelkes:

The nightingale, the organ of delight / Lassus: Tragico tecti syrmate / Handl: Trahe me post te / Hofhaimer: Tu ne quaesieris / Handl: Virgines prudentes / Hofhaimer: Vitam quae faciant beatiorem / Sweelinck: Voici du gai Printemps.

Eur *Europäische Madrigale für gleiche Stimmen.* Edited by Egon Kraus. Zürich: Pelikan (Edition 803), 1956. Obtain from Magnamusic Distributors, Sharon, Conn. Each item, except arrangements, of the complete contents given below is indexed in the body of the *List*.

Palestrina: Ahi, che quest' occhi miei / Regnart: All mein Gedanken / Marenzio: Amatemi ben mio / Widmann: Es ist ein edle Gottesgab / Othmayr: Es ist ein Schnee gefallen / Elsbeth: Freunde, so lasst uns jetzund singen / Hagius: Herzlich tut mich erfreuen / Morley: Ho who comes here? / Isaac: Hör an mein Klag / Certon: Je ne fus jamais si aise / Rauch: Ein Kellner und ein Koch / Gumpelzhaimer: Lasst fröhlich nun uns singen / Le Jeune: Ma Mignonne [two settings] / Jeep: Mein Feinslieb / Costeley: Mignonne [arr] / Clemens non Papa: Mijn hartelijk lief / Vittoria: Musik, du edle Kunst / Vittoria: Musik, schöner Klang / Hilton: My mistress frowns / Bateson: The nightingale so soon / Marenzio: Occhi dolci e soavi / Monteverdi: Qual si può dir maggiore / Géro: Quand je bois du vin clairet / Monteverdi: Raggi dov'è'l mio bene / Haussmann: Schätzlein, zu dir hat sich mein Herz gesellet / Regnart: Wenn ich gedenk der Stund / Widmann: Wohlauf, ihr Gäste / Hilton: You lovers that have loves astray.

GM *Geschichte der Musik in Beispielen.* Edited by Arnold Schering. Leipzig: Breitkopf and Härtel, 1931. Those pieces in this collection suitable for performance by women's voices are given below and indexed under composer. The entire collection contains 313 instrumental and vocal compositions.

Lassus: Adoramus te, Christe [MaO 224 (177)] /

Palestrina: Benedictus, fr Missa Lauda Sion /
Bodenschatz: De passione / Turnhout: En regardant / Ciconia: Et in terra pax / Calvisius: Ein
feste Burg / Eccles: Hark! Harry / Purcell: I gave
her cakes / Krieger: O schöne Schäferin / Salinis:
Salve regina / Regnart: Venus / Arcadelt: Voi mi
ponest'.

HAM   *Historical anthology of music. Oriental, medieval and
renaissance music.* Edited by Archibald T. Davison
and Willi Apel. Cambridge: Harvard University
Press, 1946. Those pieces in this collection suitable
for performance by women's voices are given below
and indexed under composer. The entire collection
contains 168 instrumental and vocal compositions.

Lantins: Ce ieusse fait / Ciconia: Et in terra pax /
Binchois: Files à marier / Jacopo da Bologna: Non
al suo amante / Lantins: Puisque je voy / Machaut:
S'il estoit nulz / Landini: Sy dolce non sono /
Praetorius: Vater unser.

JöG   Jöde, Fritz (ed). *Geistliche Lieder und Gesänge für
gleiche Stimmen.* Wolfenbüttel-Berlin: Georg Kall-
meyer Verlag, 1930. This collection is apparently out-
of-print, however it is included here due to its unusual
value. It is hoped that the interested reader can locate
a copy in a library. Each item of the complete contents given below is indexed under composer.

Brahms: Adoramus te / Lassus: Adoramus te /
Lassus: Agimus tibi gratias / Obrecht: Agnus Dei
/ Lassus: Alleluja, laus et gloria / Rauch: Aller
Augen warten auf dich / Martini: Als Jesus lag am
Ölberg / Praetorius: Aus tiefer Not schrei ich zu
dir / Arnold von Bruck: Ave Maria / Aichinger:
Ave Regina coelorum / Hassler: Benedictus /
Palestrina: Benedictus / Praetorius: Christ lag in
Todes Banden / Lechner: Christus ist für uns
gestorben / Caldara: Crucifixus / Hassler: Cruci-
fixus / Arnold von Bruck: Da pacem, Domine /
Staden: Danket dem Herren / Schütz: Das Blut

Jesu Christi / Albert: Das Leid ist hier / Gesius: Der du bist drei in Einigkeit / Eccard: Der Tag der ist so freudenreich / Lassus: Die Welt und all ihr Reichtum / Hassler: Ecce non dormitabit / Le Maistre: Ein feste Burg ist unser Gott / Staden: Ein jeder Mensch betrachte eben / Praetorius: Es ist gewisslich an der Zeit / Schein: Frau Nachtigall / Lechner: Freu dich heut und allezeit / Schein: Frohlocket nun, erhebet hoch / Dietrich: Gib uns heut unser täglich Brot / Hagius: Gott geb uns heut ein gute Nacht / Vento: Gott ist mein Trost / Le Maistre: Gott sei gelobet und gebenedeiet / Kugelmann: Gott Vater, Sohn, heiliger Geist / Lassus: Gross ist der Herr / Elsbeth: Harre des Herrn / Gumpelzhaimer: Helft mir Gotts Güte preisen / Lassus: Herr, der du meine Stärke bist / Schein: Herr, tu meine Lippen auf / Staden: Herr, unser Herrscher / Weiss: Heut gehn wir mit dem Kreuz und Fahn / Kugelmann: Ich dank dir fast / Gumpelzhaimer: Ich dank dir, lieber Herre / Schütz: Ich ruf zu dir, o Jesu Christ / Schütz: Ich weiss, das mein Herr Jesu Christ / Spitta: Ich wollt, dass ich daheime wär / Praetorius: In dulci jubilo / Gumpelzhaimer: In meiner Not hoff ich auf Gott / Martini: In monte Oliveti / Lassus: In pace in idipsum dormiam / Palestrina: Incipit lamentatio / Gumpelzhaimer: Ist Gott für uns / Gumpelzhaimer: Jesu, du armes Kindelein / Walther: Jesus Christus, unser Heiland / Schröter: Joseph, lieber Joseph mein / Praetorius: Komm, heiliger Geist / Staden: Lobet den Herren alle Heiden / Anon.: Mass / Gumpelzhaimer: Mit Fried und Freud fahr ich dahin / Gumpelzhaimer: Nun freuet euch, ihr Arm und Reich / Ducis: Nun freut euch, lieben Christen gmein / Praetorius: Nun komm, der Heiden Heiland / Gumpelzhaimer: O Jesu Christ, verlass uns nicht / Hagius: O Mensch, betracht / Gesius: O Vater aller Frommen / Vittoria: O vos

omnes / Palestrina: Pleni sunt coeli / Schein:
Schaffe in mir, Gott / Hassler: Siehe, es wird nicht
schlafen / Lassus: Straf mich, Herr nicht im Eifermut / Staden: Vater unser, der du bist / Vento:
Vater unser im Himmelreich / Lotti: Vere languores nostros / Palestrina: Vide Domine / Langius: Wann ich nur hab dich / Praetorius: Wenn
mein Stündlein vorhanden ist / Lassus: Wie ein
Hirsch gierlich schreien tut / Elsbeth: Wollt ich
nicht fröhlich singen / Staden: Zion spricht: Der
Herr hat mich verlassen.

JöW   Jöde, Fritz (ed). *Weltliche Lieder und Gesänge für
gleiche Stimmen.* Wolfenbüttel-Berlin: Georg Kall-
meyer Verlag, 1930. This collection is apparently out-
of-print, however it is included here due to its unusual value. It is hoped that the interested reader can
locate a copy in a library. Each item of the complete
contents given below, except arrangements, is indexed
under composer.

Scandellus: Ach Gott, wem soll ich klagen / Reg-
nart: Ach Gott, wie soll ich singen / Lechner: Ach
Lieb, ich muss dich lassen / Schaerer: Ach Schei-
dens Art / Regnart: All mein Gedanken / Langius:
Allein das bittre Scheiden / Gosswin: Am Abend
spat / Haussmann: Annelein sein / Locatello: Dein
Äuglein leuchten / Eccard: Der Kuckuck auf dem
Dache sass / Schein: Der kühle Maien / Morley:
Der Lenz all Äst bekleiden tut / Albert: Der Nord-
wind lässt sich hören / Regnart: Der süsse Schlaf /
Clemens non Papa: Der Winter ist ein unwert Gast
/ Gumpelzhaimer: Die dunkle Nacht ist über uns
gekommen / Gosswin: Die Fassnacht ist ein schöne
Zeit / Gumpelzhaimer: Die finster Nachte nun ver-
geht / Albert: Die Sonne rennt mit Prangen / Le
Maistre: Die Wahrheit ist gen Himmel geflogen /
Regnart: Dies ist die Zeit, die mich erfreut / Ha-
gius: Du bist ein Gottesgabe / Zangius: Ducke
dich, Hänsel / Gosswin: Ein guter Wein ist Lobes

wert / Lechner: Ein jeder meint, er sei der best /
Rauch: Ein Kellner und ein Koch / Haussmann:
Ein lieblicher Wein / Erpf: Einmal nur in unserm
Leben / Lechner: Elend bringt Pein / Vento:
Entlaubet ist der Walde / Gerhardt: Erde, die uns
dies gebracht / Medici: Es liebet mir das Jagen /
Hagius: Es stehet geschrieben / Apiarius: Es taget
vor dem Walde / Rosthius: Frau Nachtigall, mach
dich bereit / Haussmann: Frisch ist mein Sinn /
Morley: Gegrüsst seid, ihr Nymphen [arr] / Regnart: Glaub nit, dass ich könnt dein so gar vergessen / Lechner: Glück, führ, zurück / Lechner:
Grün ist der Mai / Lechner: Gut Singer und ein
Organist / Hagius: Herzlich tut mich erfreuen /
Steuccius: Herzliebstes Liebelein / Lechner: Hört,
was sich hat zutragen / Anon.: Ich armes Mägdlein
klag mein Pein / Sartorius: Ich hab mir auserkoren
/ Joh. Schultze: Ich und du / Regnart: Ich wollt,
wer mir mein Glück nicht gönnt / Gastoldi: In
eurer Lieb bin ich / Isaac: Innsbruck, ich muss dich
lassen / Vecchi: Ist nicht einer vorhanden / Lechner: Jagen, Hetzen und Federspiel / Schein: Ki-
keriki! Kakakanei! / Widmann: Kommt her, ihr
Herrn Studenten frei / Marenzio: Kommt, ihr
lieblichen Stimmen alle / Langius: Lenz kommt
herbei / Rosthius: Lieblich wohl kommt der Mai /
Haussmann: Mein edle Kaiserinne / Gastoldi:
Mein Gdanken tun mich zwingen / Lechner: Mein
grosse Lieb, die macht mich blind / Regnart: Mein
Mund der singt / Medici: Mein Schätzlein ist von
Flandern / Haussmann: Mein trautes Liebelein /
Zangius: Mir gliebt im grünen Maien / Friderici:
Mit Lust will ich mein Zeit zubringen / Hauss-
mann: Mit Seufzen und mit Klag / Regnart: Nach
meiner Lieb viel hundert Knaben trachten /
Marenzio: O holdseliges Herze / Vento: Ob ich
schon arm und elend bin / Lechner: Scheiden von
Lieb und das tut weh / Harnisch: So wünsch ich

ihr ein gute Nacht / Schaerer: So wünsch ich ihr ein gute Nacht / Palestrina: Soll ich denn meiden dich / Haussmann: Soviel man Wasserwellen / Dedekind: Trink ich Wein, so verderb ich / Anon.: Tröst mich, mein Lieb / Eccard: Unsre lieben Hühnerchen / Schein: Viel schöner Blümelein / Marenzio: Von eim fliessenden Brunnen / Gumpelzhaimer: Wacht auf, ihr lieben Vögelein / Morley: Warum nicht lustig? / de Sayve: Warum willst du nicht fröhlich sein? / Lechner: Was will ich mehr von ihr? / Harnisch: Weil ich gross Gunst trag zu der Kunst / Harnisch: Wenn ich seh deiner Äuglein Schein / Petrejus: Wer das Elend bauen will / Widmann: Wer Lust und Lieb zur Musik hat / Schaerer: Wer lützel hat und viel vertut / Dedekind: Wer will mir helfen klagen? / Schaerer: Wie schön blüht uns der Maie / Haussmann: Wie sehr ich mich um Lieb nehm an / Hilton: Willkommen, holder Musikklang / Petrejus: Wir sind bereit zur Winterszeit / Marenzio: Wo ist der Tag hinkommen? / Schaerer: Wo soll ich mich hinkehren? / Anon.: Wohlauf, ihr lieben Gsellen / Widmann: Wohlauf, Soldatenblut / Haussmann: Zu Ehren will ich singen / Steuccius: Zwölftausend Mägdelein.

Lei   Leichtentritt, Hugo (ed). *Geistliche Frauenchöre alter Meister*. 4 vols. Leipzig: Steingräber-Verlag, 1911. These collections may not be easily available, but are included here due to their unusual value. It is hoped that the interested reader can locate copies in a library. The contents of volumes I and II are indexed under composers.

Vol. I. Aichinger: Assumpta est / Bruck: Ave Maria / Aichinger: Ave Regina / Mahu: Christ ist erstanden / Bruck: Da pacem, Domine / Bruck: Pater noster.

Vol. II. Palestrina: Adoramus / Palestrina: Ave Regina / Palestrina: Benedictus / Palestrina: Cruci-

fixus / Palestrina: Crucifixus / Palestrina: Pueri
Hebraeorum.

*The Morning star choir book. A collection of unison
and two-part music for treble or male voices.* Compiled and edited by Paul Thomas. St. Louis: Concordia (Edition 97–6287), 1957. There are 28 original
compositions and arrangements usually with keyboard accompaniment. All are in English only. The
complete contents, given below, are not indexed in
this *List*.

Mozart: Alleluia [canon] / Lenel: All praise to God
who reigns above / Buxtehude: Arise, sons of the
kingdom / Franck: Ascended is our God and Lord
/ Bouman: Behold, the Lamb of God / Bach: Beside Thy manger here I stand / Bender: Built on
the rock the Church doth stand / Wolff: Come,
Holy Spirit, come / Bender: Come, ye faithful,
raise the strain / Handel: Daughter of Zion / Willan: Glory be to God on high / Vierdanck: Glory
to God in the highest / Gumpeltzhaimer: Go ye
into all the world / Willan: Holy, holy, holy /
Schop: How lovely shines the morning star / Bach:
Jesus, refuge of the weary / Bach: Let all the multi-
tudes of light / Lenel: Loving shepherd of the sheep
/ Bender: O Christ, thou Lamb of God / Marcello:
Oh, hold thou me up / Brahms: O Jesus, joy of
loving hearts / Bach: The only Son from heaven /
Wolff: Sing with joy, glad voices lift / Buxtehude:
To God the anthem raising / Greene: Thou visitest
the earth / Vaughan Williams: Unto Him that
loved us / Tunder: Wake, awake, for night is fly-
ing / Pachelbel: What God ordains is always good.

MET *Music of earlier times. Vocal and instrumental ex-
amples, 13th Century to Bach.* Edited by Johannes
Wolf. New York: Broude Bros., 1946. This is an
American reprint of *Sing- und Spielmusik aus älterer
Zeit*. The pieces in this collection suitable for per-
formance by women's voices are given below and in-

dexed under composer. The complete collection contains 65 instrumental and vocal pieces.

Anon.: Antiphona—Constantes / Luzzaschi: Cor mio / Kugelmann: Grates nunc / Lechner: Gut Singer / Grenon: Je ne requier / Landino: El mie / Nicolaus: Passando / Anon.: Por la puente / Anon.: Salve virgo / Dufay: Veni creator spiritus / Anon.: Vergine bella.

Neue Weihnachtslieder. Chor-Ausgabe für gleiche Stimmen. Kassel and Basel: Bärenreiter-Verlag (Edition Bä 1372), 1962. This is a collection of 34 Christmas compositions, easy to medium-difficult, mostly by modern composers. All are for SSA, unaccompanied, with German text only. The complete contents, given below, are not indexed under composer.

Knorr: Als die Hirten auf dem Felde / Knorr: Als ein behutsam Licht / Schwarz: Also liebt Gott die arge Welt / Knorr: Banger Mensch in deine Nacht / Schwarz: Baum der Erkenntnis des Guten und Bösen / Knorr: Da die Hirten ihre Herden / Burkhard: Das Reich ist dein, Herr Jesu Christ / Micheelsen: Der du die Welt geschaffen hast / Schwarz: Der unser aller Heil und Hirt / Petzold: Die Nacht ist vorgedrungen / Schwarz: Du Kind, zu dieser heiligen Zeit / Schwarz: Ein Kindlein ist uns geboren / Schwarz: Ein Kindlein liegt im armen Stall / Schwarz: Es ist ein Schnee gefallen / Lahusen: Es lagen im Felde die Hirten bei Nacht / Knorr: Friede auf Erden / Marx: Ich will dem Knäblein schenken / Lahusen: Jahr, dein Haupt neig / Lahusen: Lasst eure bittren Klagen sein / Lahusen: Mein Hirt, vernahmest du schon / Lahusen: Mit Schall von Zungen / Gneist: Nun juble laut all Kreatur / Schwarz: Nun juble laut und freue dich / Lahusen: Nun vergesst der Traurigkeit / Gerhardt: Oft, wenn ich mich kränke / Gneist: O Jesukind, komm zu uns her / Lahusen: O Kindlein mein / Micheelsen: Steht auf und wacht, der Morgen lacht / Lahusen: Steht auf und wacht, der Morgen lacht / Micheelsen: Trittst du wieder vor die Nacht / Lahusen: Wir harren, Christ, in dunkler Zeit / Gerhardt: Wir hielten auf dem Felde Wacht / Lahusen: Wisst ihr noch, wie es geschehen / Lahusen: Zur stillen Nacht.

Das Quempas-Heft. Auslese deutscher Weihnachtslieder. Ausgabe für gleiche Stimmen. Edited by Konrad Ameln. Kassel and Basel: Bärenreiter-Verlag (Edition Bä 1302), 1962. This is a collection of 35 Christmas compositions, easy to medium-difficult, by old and modern composers. Most are for three equal voices, all are unaccompanied, and all are with German text only. The complete contents, given below, are not indexed under composer.

Schwarz: Auf, auf! Ihr Buben steht alle gschwind auf / Chemin-Petit: Christum wir sollen loben schon / Chemin-Petit: Den die Hirten lobeten sehre / Hensel: Der Heiland ist geboren / Eccard: Der Tag der ist so freudenreich / Lahusen: Ein Kind geborn zu Bethlehem / Marx: Ein Kind ist uns geboren heut / Schwarz: Es ist ein Ros entsprungen / Thate: Es ist geborn ein Kindelein / Distler: Es kommt ein Schiff, geladen / Marx: Freut euch, freut euch all insgemein / Thate: Freut euch, ihr lieben Christen all / Micheelsen: Fröhlich soll mein Herze springen / Pepping: Geborn ist uns ein Kindelein / Hoyoul: Gelobet seist Du, Jesu Christ / Gerhardt: Ich steh an deiner Krippen hier / Praetorius: In dulci jubilo / Thate: In einem Kripplein lag ein Kind / Micheelsen: Joseph, lieber Joseph mein / Schwarz: Kommet, ihr Hirten, ihr Männer und Frain / Pepping: Kommt und lasst uns Christum ehren / Distler: Lobt Gott, ihr Christen, alle gleich / Schwarz: Lobt Gott, ihr Christen, alle gleich / Chemin-Petit: Macht hoch die Tür / Thate: Nun freut euch lieben Kinderlein / Praetorius: Nun komm, der Heiden Heiland

/ Pepping: Nun singet und seid froh / Distler: O Heiland, reiss die Himmel auf / Ameln: Singet frisch und wohlgemut / Marx: Uns ist ein Kindlein heut geborn / Othmayr: Vom Himmel hoch da komm ich her / Pepping: Vom Himmel hoch, o Englein kommt / Gerhardt: Vom Himmel kam der Engel Schar / Pepping: Wach Nachtigall, wach auf / Pepping: Wunderbarer Gnadenthron.

RWOM   *Responses from the works of old masters.* Edited by E. Harold Geer. E. C. Schirmer (ES 869). Each item of the complete contents given below is indexed under composer.

Handl: Christus factus est / Palestrina: Gloria Patri / Menegali: Jesu, salvator / Byrd [sic]: Non nobis.

The SSA chorale book. Edited by Paul Thomas. St. Louis: Concordia (Edition 97-7592), 1960. The collection contains 32 easy to medium-difficult choral settings by old and modern composers. All are in English only. The complete contents, given below, are not indexed under composer.

Praetorius: A child is born in Bethlehem / Greitter: A lamb goes uncomplaining forth / Decius: All glory be to God on high / Teschner: All glory, laud, and honor / Strube: Beautiful savior / Strube: Come, Holy Ghost, God and Lord / Strube: The day is surely drawing near / Chemin-Petit: Dear Christians, one and all, rejoice / Strube: From heaven above to earth I come / Willan: Hail the day that sees Him rise / Metzler: How lovely shines the morning star / Strube: If thou but suffer God to guide thee / Strube: Jesus Christ, my sure defense / Petzold: Jesus, priceless treasure / Strube: Let our gladness know no end / Petzold: Let us ever walk with Jesus / Vulpius: Lo, how a rose e'er blooming [canon] / Hennig: Lord, keep us steadfast in thy word / Strube: Now thank we all our

God / Strube: O dearest Jesus, what law hast thou broken / Kindermann: O Jesus, my Lord, my God / Anon.: The only Son from heaven / Strube: O sinner, come thy sin to mourn / Vogel: Praise God the Lord / Weber: Praise to the Lord, the almighty / Strube: Salvation unto us has come / Petzold: Savior of the nations, come / Strube: Sing to the Lord of harvest / Scheidt: Triune God, be thou our stay [canon] / Strube: Wake, awake, for night is flying / Strube: We all rejoice on this glad day / Abraham: We now implore God the Holy Ghost / Strube: Ye sons and daughters of the King / Strube: Ye sons of men, oh, hearken.

Ste Stevens, Georgia (ed). *Mediaeval and renaissance choral music for equal voices a cappella.* Boston: McLaughlin and Reilly Company, 1940. Each item of the complete contents given below, except folksongs and unison compositions, is indexed under composer.

Anon. circa 995: Hymn of St. Adalbert [unison] / Anon. Chartres: Alleluia-Angelus Domini / Anon. 13th C: Alleluia Psallat / Taverner: Audivi / Lassus: Benedictus / Anon. Spanish: Catalan folk songs / Ott: Dies est laetitiae / Dufay: Flos florum / Anon. 1349: German flagellants' hymn [unison] / Taverner: Gloria in excelsis / Leoninus: Haec dies / Vittoria: Judas mercator / Animuccia: Kyrie / Obrecht: Missa sine nomine / Anon. 13th C: O miranda Dei caritas / Ott: On this our joyful holiday / Anon. 13th C: Puellare gremium / Palestrina: Pueri hebraeorum / Dunstable: Quam pulchra es / Obrecht: Qui cum patre / Tallis: Sancte Deus / Anon.: Sanctus [unison] / Vittoria: Una hora.

Tov Tovey, Donald (ed). *Laudate Pueri. Sacred music of the XVIth century* [sic]. London: Augener (Edition 9169), 1910. Each title of this collection is also available from the publisher separately. Each item of the complete contents given below is indexed under composer.

Vittoria: Accende lumen sensibus / Lassus: Adoramus te / Lassus: Adoramus te / Agostini: Adoramus te / Palestrina: Adoramus te / Lassus: Agimus tibi gratias / Lassus: Agimus tibi gratias / Lassus: Alleluja laus et gloria / Mozart: Alleluja / Mozart: Ave Maria / Palestrina: Benedictus qui venit / Palestrina: Benedictus qui venit / Lassus: Benedictus qui venit / Vittoria: Christe eleison / Costantini: Confitemini Domino / Palestrina: Confitemini Domino / Gabrieli: Crucifixus / Palestrina: Crucifixus / Vittoria: Duo seraphim / Croce: Et resurrexit / Lassus: Expandi manus / Lassus: Hodie apparuit in Israel / Palestrina: Hodie Christus natus est / Lassus: Ipsa te cogat pietas / Lassus: In pace in idipsum dormiam / Palestrina: Jesu Rex admirabilis / Mozart: Kyrie eleison / Lassus: Oculus non vidit / Vittoria: O sacrum convivium / Vittoria: O vos omnes / Palestrina: Pleni sunt coeli / Palestrina: Salve Regina / Lassus: Sancti mei / Palestrina: Tua Jesu dilectio.

We praise Thee II. A choir book for the church year. By Healey Willan. St. Louis: Concordia (Edition 97–7610), 1962. This collection contains 23 unison, two-part, and three-part anthems and motets for the entire church year. All are in English and easy to easy-medium, with keyboard accompaniment. The complete contents, given below, are not indexed under composer.

At the name of Jesus / Behold, I send my messenger / Bless we the Father, the Son, and the Holy Ghost / Christ, our passover / God be merciful unto us / I am the Resurrection and the life / I was glad / I will not leave you comfortless / Lift up your heads, O ye gates / Lo, the star which they saw / Magnificat / Make a joyful noise unto the Lord / Now are ye light in the Lord / Nunc dimittis / Oh, send out Thy light / Oh, sing unto the Lord a new song / Rejoice in the Lord alway / The responsory for

Passiontide / The seed is the word of God / Surely
He hath borne our griefs / Verily, verily I say unto
you / When the herds were watching / The word
was made flesh.

Whit   Whittaker, W. Gillies (ed). *The Oxford graduated
round book.* Oxford University Press, 1937. The complete contents are given below. Those rounds by
Beethoven, Haydn, Mozart, and Schubert have been
indexed in the body of the *List.* References Pammelia,
Deuteromelia, and Melismata are to Ravenscroft's
editions of 1609, 1609, and 1611, respectively.

Pammelia: Lady, come down and see / Haydn:
Guter Rat / Pammelia: The white hen / Pammelia:
The old dog / Deuteromelia: Hold thy peace /
Whittaker: Well-a-day / Melismata: Derry ding
ding / Pammelia: Joan, come kiss me now /
Deuteromelia: The great bells of Oseney / Haydn:
Fester Sinn / Pammelia: O praise the Lord / Pam-
melia: Grant us all Thy mercy / Pammelia: Praise
God almighty / Mozart: Difficile lectu / Schubert:
Willkommen, lieber schöner Mai / Beethoven:
Ewig dein / Schubert: Goldner Schein / Beethoven:
Im Arm der Liebe ruht sich's wohl / Pammelia:
Jolly shepherd / Pammelia: The nightingale /
Beethoven: Ars longa / Deuteromelia: O my love
/ Haydn: Das Hexen-Einmal-Eins / Haydn: Zuruf
/ Haydn: Weisheit / Beethoven: Glück / Haydn:
Die liebe Maienzeit / Beethoven: An Mälzel /
Haydn: Herr Gänsewitz zu seinem Kammerdiener
/ Pammelia: Pray and work / Pammelia: Farewell /
Melismata: Kit and Tom / Haydn: Ersatz / Haydn:
Wein, Liebe, Gesang.

Das Wochenlied. Edited by Philipp Reich. Kassel and
Basel: Bärenreiter-Verlag (Edition Bä 2209), 1952.
This is a collection of 140 choral settings, mostly by
modern composers, easy or medium-difficult. All are
unaccompanied, with German text. Most chorales
have a setting for 2 equal voices (by the first composer

given) and a setting for 3 equal voices (by the second composer given). The complete contents, given below, are not indexed under composer.

Zipp: Paminger: Ach bleib bei uns, Herr Jesu Christ / Reda: Zipp: Thate: Ach Gott vom Himmel sieh darein / Zipp: Raphael: Allein zu dir, Herr Jesu Christ / Schwarz: Schwarz: Das alte Jahr vergangen ist / Bender: Schwarz: Auf diesen Tag bedenken wir / Driessler: Hessenberg: Auf meinen lieben Gott / Marx: Distler: Aus tiefer Not schrei ich zu dir / Hessenberg: Thate: Aus tiefer Not schrei ich zu dir / Baur: Beyer: Reda: Christe, du Beistand deiner Kreuzgemeine / Raphael: Schwarz: Christ lag in Todesbanden / Hessenberg: Stern: Christ unser Herr zum Jordan kam / Driessler: Marx: Du grosser Schmerzensmann / Raphael: Zipp: Durch Adams Fall ist ganz verderbt / Knab: Schwarz: Es ist das Heil uns kommen her / Thate: Knab: Es ist gewisslich an der Zeit / Hessenberg: Bornefeld: Es wolle Gott uns gnädig sein / Zipp: Hoyoul: Gelobet seist du, Jesu Christ / Zipp: Petzold: Gott der Vater wohn uns bei / Schwarz: de la Motte: Gottes Sohn ist kommen / Driessler: Bornefeld: Heilger Geist, du Tröster mein / Marx: Anon. 1541: Herr Christ, der einig Gotts Sohn / Schwarz: Micheelsen: Herr Gott, dich loben alle wir / Fiebig: Bender: Der Herr ist mein getreuer Hirt / Micheelsen: Baur: Herzlich lieb hab ich dich, o Herr / Walcha: Koch: Ich ruf zu dir, Herr Jesu Christ / Zipp: Ruppel: Ich weiss, mein Gott, dass all mein Tun / Schmidt: Marx: Ihr lieben Christen, freut euch nun / Micheelsen: Ruppel: In dich hab ich gehoffet, Herr / Stier: Wenzel: Jesu, meine Freude / Driessler: Koch: Jesu, nun sei gepreiset / Schmidt: Dietrich: Jesus Christus, unser Heiland, der den Tod / Schwarz: Ruppel: Jesus Christus, unser Heiland, der von uns / Stern: Brod: Komm, Gott Schöpfer, Heiliger Geist / Weiss: Thate: Komm, Heiliger Geist, Herre Gott / Degen:

de la Motte: Kommt her zu mir, spricht Gottes
Sohn / Schwarz: Gerhardt: Ein Lämmlein geht und
trägt die Schuld / Gottschick: Driessler: Lasset uns
mit Jesu ziehen / Petzold: Raphael: Lobt Gott den
Herrn, ihr Heiden all / Bornefeld: Zipp: Mit Ernst,
o Menschenkinder / Gerhardt: Distler: Mit Freuden zart zu dieser Fahrt / Stern: Schwarz: Mitten
wir im Leben sind / Walcha: Zipp: Nimm von uns,
Herr, du treuer Gott / Zipp: Bender: Nun bitten
wir den Heiligen Geist / Driessler: Bender: Nun
freut euch, lieben Christen gmein / Bender: Bornefeld: Nun jauchzet, all ihr Frommen / Driessler:
Stern: Nun komm, der Heiden Heiland / Kraft:
Gerhardt: Nun lasst uns Gott dem Herren / Marx:
Neumeyer: Nun lob, mein Seel, den Herren / Petzold: Schwarz: Nun preiset alle Gottes Barmherzig-
keit / Zipp: Weiss: O gläubig Herz, gebenedei /
Wenzel: Zipp: O König Jesu Christe / Schwarz:
Neumeyer: O Mensch, bewein dein Sünde gross /
Kraft: Hessenberg: O süsser Herre Jesu Christ /
Hessenberg: Brod: Preis, Lob und Dank sei Gott
dem Herren / Petzold: Thate: Sei Lob und Ehr
dem höchsten Gut / Hessenberg: Micheelsen: Such,
wer da will, ein ander Ziel / Hessenberg: Raphael:
Valet will ich dir geben / Othmayr: Paminger:
Vater unser im Himmelreich / Othmayr: Zipp:
Vom Himmel kam der Engel Schar / A. Wagner:
Degen: Von Gott will ich nicht lassen / Bornefeld:
Schwarz: Wach auf, wach auf, du deutsches Land /
Driessler: Dietrich: Wachet auf, ruft uns die Stimme
/ Marx: Fiebig: Wär Gott nicht mit uns diese Zeit /
Thate: Schwarz: Was mein Gott will, das gscheh
allzeit / Thate: Crappius: Wenn wir in höchsten
Nöten sein / Schwarz: Hessenberg: Wie schön
leuchtet der Morgenstern / Zipp: Schwarz: Wir
glauben all an einen Gott / Zipp: Figulus: Wo
Gott der Herr nicht bei uns hält / Raphael: Stern:
Wunderbarer Gnadenthron.

SECTION THREE

Indices

flourished before 1163	Leoninus
c. 1237–1287	Adam de la Halle
14th C	Jacopo da Bologna
c. 1300–1377	Guillaume Machaut
1325–1397	Francesco Landini
flourished c. 1360–c. 1375	Nicolaus Praepositus
flourished c. 1400	Johannes Ciconia
c. 1370–1453	John Dunstable
15th C, first half	Johannes Brasart
15th C	Robert Chirbury
15th C	Grenon
c. 1400–1467	Gilles de Binchois
c. 1400–1472	Guillaume Dufay
c. 1420–?	Byttering
c. 1420–?	Hubertus de Salinis
flourished c. 1450	Hugo de Lantins
1430–1495	Johannes Ockeghem
c. 1445–1521	Josquin Després
c. 1445–1529	Jacotin (Jacques Godebrye)
1449–1492	Lorenzo Medici
1450–1505	Jacob Obrecht
c. 1450–1517	Heinrich Isaac
late 15th C	William Newark
15th–16th C	Dr. Robert Cooper
1459–1537	Paul Hofhaimer
c. 1480–1544	Benedict Ducis
between 1480/90–1562	Adrian Willaert
c. 1485–after 1546	Nikolaus Decius
?–before 1544	Stephan Mahu
?–1549?	Johann Ott
?–1550	Johann Petrejus
c. 1490–1542 or 1543	Ludwig Senfl
c. 1490–1548	Sixtus Dietrich
c. 1490–1562	Claude de Sermisy
c. 1495–1545	John Taverner
1496–1570	Johann Walter
1500–1553	Matthias Apiarius
c. 1500–1553	Cristobal Morales
c. 1500–1554	Arnold von Bruck
c. 1500–1571	Giovanni Animuccia

?–1542	Johannes Kugelmann
?–1567	Jakob Vaet
c. 1505–1572	Claude Goudimel
c. 1505–1585	Thomas Tallis
c. 1510–1555/56	Clemens non Papa
c. 1510–1572	Pierre Certon
c. 1510–1586	Andrea Gabrieli
c. 1514–after 1557	Jacob Arcadelt
1515–1553	Kaspar Othmayr
1517–1580	Antonius Scandellus
1519–1545	Costanzo Festa
flourished 1550	Herbert Lecouteux
c. 1520–c. 1563	John Shepperd
?–1577	Mattheus le Maistre
c. 1520–1580	Gerard Turnhout
1520?–1591	Joan Brudieu
1525–1594	Giovanni Pierluigi da Palestrina
1528–c. 1600	Claude le Jeune
?–1587	Gregor Langius
1530 or 1532–1594	Orlando de Lassus
c. 1532–1595	Leonhart Schröter
c. 1540–1575	Ivo de Vento
c. 1540–1594	Anton Gosswin
1540–1599	Jakob Regnart
1542–1623	Andreas Crappius
1542/43–1623	William Byrd
1545–1607	Giovanni Maria Nanini
c. 1549–1611	Tomás Luis de Vittoria
1549–1614	Lambert de Sayve
1550–1591	Jacob Hándl (Gallus)
c. 1550–1592	Marco Antonio Ingegneri
1550–1605	Orazio Vecchi
c. 1550–1606	Leonhard Lechner
c. 1550–1620	Conrad Hagius
16th C	Giovanni Battista Locatello
16th C	Jean Géro
?–before 1620	Nicolaus Zangius
1553–1599	Luca Marenzio
1553–1611	Johann Eccard
1556–1615	Sethus Calvisius
1556–1622	Giovanni Gastoldi

1557–1603	Thomas Morley
?–after 1611	Valentin Haussmann
16th–17th C	Domenico Massentio
16th–17th C	Henry Youll
?–c. 1607	Luzzasco Luzzaschi
1559–1625	Adam Gumpeltzhaimer
c. 1560–1609	Giovanni Croce
c. 1560–c. 1613	Bartholomeus Gesius
flourished 1597	William Holborne
1562–1621	Jean Pieterszoon Sweelinck
1564–1612	Hans Leo Hassler
1564–1627	L. C. da Viadana
1564–1628	Gregor Aichinger
c. 1565–1630	John Danyel
1567–1620	Thomas Campian
1567–1648	Claudio Monteverdi
c. 1570–1614	John Bennet
c. 1570–1630	Thomas Bateson
1571–1621	Michael Praetorius
?–1630	Ott Siegfried Harnisch
flourished c. 1600	Nicolaus Rosthius
flourished c. 1600	Andreas Rauch
flourished 1607	Robert Jones
?–after 1624	Thomas Elsbeth
?–after 1628	Henning Dedekind
1573–1656	Thomas Tomkins
1574?–1607	Ivan Lukačić
1574–1634	Erasmus Widmann
1574–1638	John Wilbye
c. 1575–1623	Thomas Weelkes
c. 1575–1628	Alfonso Ferrabosco
?–1630	Alessandro de' Grandi
1575–1630	Richard Dering
1576–1636	Erhard Bodenschatz
1578–1640	Agostino Agazzari
c. 1580–1629	Paulo Agostini
1580–1638	Daniel Friderici
1580–1648	Michael East
1581–1634	Johann Staden
1581–1644	Johann Jeep
1582–1645	William Lawes

before 1585–before 1641	John Ward
before 1585–1653	Johannes Schultze
before 1585–?	Paulus Sartorius
before 1585–?	Melchior Schaerer
flourished c. 1606–1610	John Bartlet
c. 1585–?	Heinrich Steuccius
1585–1672	Heinrich Schütz
1586–1630	Johann Hermann Schein
c. 1590–1655	Tarquinio Merula
1592–1640	Thomas Ravenscroft
c. 1593–1637	Heinrich Grimm
1595–1662	Henry Lawes
1595–1673/4	John Wilson
1598–1653	Luigi Rossi
1599–1657	John Hilton
1604–1651	Heinrich Albert
1611–?	Thomas Brewer
1614–1698	Benjamin Rogers
c. 1615–1687	John Gamble
1616–1655	Johann Erasmus Kindermann
1623–1686	John Playford
?–1676	Joan Cererols
1632–1677	Matthew Locke
1634–1666	Adam Krieger
1634–1704	Marc Antoine Charpentier
c. 1643–?	Alessandro Costantini
17th C	Johann Vierdanck
1654–1740	Vincent Lübeck
1658–1695	Henry Purcell
1663–1733	François Couperin
1665–1729	Francesco Gasperini
c. 1667–1740	Antonio Lotti
1668–1735	John Eccles
c. 1670–?	Claudio Casciolini
1670–1736	Antonio Caldara
1685–1750	Johann Sebastian Bach
1685–1759	Georg Friedrich Handel
1685–1767	Niccola Porpora
1686–1739	Benedetto Marcello
1695–1755	Maurice Greene
1699–1783	Johann Adolf Hasse

1706–1784	Giovanni Battista Martini
1710–1736	Giovanni Battista Pergolesi
1710–1778	Thomas Augustine Arne
1710–1779	William Boyce
1720–1775 or 1777	Andrea Basili
1721–1780	Francis Hutchinson (pseud. Francis Ireland)
1727–1816	Henry Harrington
1732–1809	Franz Joseph Haydn
1737–1806	Michael Haydn
1738–1797	Philip Hayes
1738–1817	Marquis of Blandford
1740–1816	Samuel Webbe
1740–1820	Joseph Corfe
1741–1790	Thomas Norris
1744–1777	Richard Woodward
1746–1800	William Billings
1756–1791	Wolfgang Amadeus Mozart
1760–1842	Luigi Cherubini
1765–1838	Thomas Attwood
1767–1850	Francesco Basili
1769–1837	Valentino Fioravanti
18th C	Lorenzo Baini
1770–1827	Ludwig van Beethoven
1775–1844	Giuseppe Baini
1784–1851	Martin J. Menegali
1792–1868	Moritz Hauptmann
1792–1868	Gioacchino Rossini
1797–1828	Franz Schubert
1801–1862	de Lafage
1803–1869	Hector Berlioz
1809–1847	Felix Mendelssohn
1810–1856	Robert Schumann
1811–1886	Franz Liszt
1813–1883	Richard Wagner
1813–1901	Giuseppe Verdi
1822–1890	César Franck
1824–1910	Carl Reinecke
1828–1908	François Auguste Gevaert
1833–1897	Johannes Brahms
1841–1894	Emmanuel Chabrier

1886–	Cyril Winn
1887–	Ernst Toch
1888–1947	John Gerrard Williams
1888–1963	Werner Josten
1890–1955	Bohuslav Martinu
1890–	Ernest Bullock
1890–	Hans Gál
1890–	Lee Pattison
1890–	Adolfo Salazar
1891–	Richard Donovan
1891–	Hermann Erpf
1891–	Timothy Mather Spelman
1892–1951	Felix Petyrek
1892–1955	Arthur Honegger
1892–	Hendrik Andriessen
1892–	Darius Milhaud
1893–1918	Lili Boulanger
1893–1955	Walter Rein
1893–	Douglas Moore
1894–1920	Philip Heseltine (pseud. Peter Warlock)
1894–	Christopher Thomas
1895–1963	Paul Hindemith
1895–	Mario Castelnuovo-Tedesco
1895–	Gordon Jacob
1895–	Ernst Levy
1895–	Leo Sowèrby
1896–1955	Josip Slavenski
1896–	Howard Hanson
1896–	Hugo Herrmann
1896–	Virgil Thomson
1897–	Henry Cowell
1897–	Camil van Hulse
1897–	Hans Lang
1897–	Karl Marx
1898–	Ernst Bacon
1898–	Roy Harris
1899–1963	Francis Poulenc
1899–	John Duke
1899–	Harl McDonald
1899–	Marcelle de Manziarly

1899–	Domingo Santa Cruz
1899–	Randall Thompson
1899–	Helmuth Weiss
1900–1960	Isadore Freed
1900–	Aaron Copland
1900–	Carl Gerhardt
1900–	Ernst Křenek
1900–	Otto Luening
1900–	Eric Thiman
1901–	Ernst Pepping
1901–	Edmund Rubbra
1902–	Hans Friedrich Micheelsen
1902–	Heinrich Spitta
1903–	Claude Arrieu
1903–	Vladimir Dukelsky
1903–	Robin Milford
1903–	Flor Peeters
1904–	H. K. Andrews
1904–	Herbert Inch
1904–	Merrill Knighton
1904–	Kurt Thomas
1905–1945?	Fritz Dietrich
1905–	Paul Csonka
1905–	Walter Kraft
1905–	William Pearson
1906–	Ross Lee Finney
1906–	Normand Lockwood
1906–	Robert L. Sanders
1906–	Grace Williams
1907–	Henry Leland Clarke
1907–	Mozart Camargo Guarnieri
1907–	Burrill Phillips
1908–1942	Hugo Distler
1908–	Elliott Carter
1908–	Richard T. Gore
1908–	Richard Warner
1909–	Harald Genzmer
1909–	Hubert Lamb
1909–	John Raynor
1910–	Samuel Barber
1910–	Lehman Engel

1910–	Jan Mul
1910–	William Schuman
1910–	Eugene Weigel
1910–	E. J. White
1911–	Mary Chandler
1911–	Alan Hovhannes
1911–	Lionel Nowak
1912–	Herman Strategier
1913–	Benjamin Britten
1913–	Norman Dello Joio
1913–	Alvin Etler
1913–	Han van Koert
1913–	Jan Meyerowitz
1913–	Gardner Read
1914–1962	Irving Fine
1915–	David Diamond
1915–	Vincent Persichetti
1916–	Albert Harris
1916–	Siegfried Reda
1917–	Walter Hendl
1917–	Ulysses Kay
1917–	William P. Latham
1918–	Victoria Glaser
1918–	J. Curtis Shake
1918–	Richard Winslow
1919–	Theron Kirk
1921–	William Bergsma
1921–	Adrian Cruft
1921–	Leland Forsblad
1921–	Leo Smit
1922–	John Boda
1922–	George Walker
1923–	Donald Lybbert
1923–	Marian McLaughlin
1923–	Peter Mennin
1923–	Daniel Pinkham
1923–	Ned Rorem
1924–	Arthur Frackenpohl
1927–	Ron Nelson
1928–	Eugene Hemmer
1929–	Colin Hand

1929–	Edwin London
1929–	Frank Speeding
1931–	Harold Brown
1931–	Jonathan Elkus
1938–	Thomas Beveridge

No dates located

Philip Cranmer   J. M. Joseph
Alfred Grant Goodman   Jan Kok
Karis Guinness   Anne Megarey
J. Alban Hinton   Russell Smith

INDEX OF COMPOSITIONS BY CATEGORIES

Below are choruses for women's voices listed by categories:

A. Duration 5–10 minutes.
B. Duration 10–15 minutes.
C. Duration 15 minutes or more.
D. With Instruments (other than keyboard), optional.
E. With Orchestra, chamber (brass, strings, etc.).
F. With Orchestra, full.
G. With Solo(s), women.
H. With Solo(s), men.

When considering optional instrumentation, it should be remembered that it is quite suitable to double a voice part, or to assign a voice part to an instrument in Mediaeval and Renaissance compositions.

In those cases where there may be difficulty in identifying which piece is being cited in this index, the title is given.

To locate Masses, Magnificats, etc., the Index of First Lines and Titles should suffice.

A. DURATION 5–10 MINUTES. Andrews / Bartók, *Wedding* / Boulanger / Brahms, *Op. 12; Op. 27* / Chabrier / Diamond / Donovan / Dufay, *Magnificat* / Duke / Freed / Goodman / Greene / Harris, A. / Harris, R. / Holst, *Ave Maria; Rig Veda* / Honegger / Kodály, *Epiphany* / Levy / Lockwood / Lybbert / McDonald / Mahler / Mendelssohn, *Surrexit* / Milhaud / Mozart, *Kyrie* / Porpora / Roger-Ducasse / Schubert, *Op. 133; Op. 134; Op. 135; Gesang der Geister; Das grosse Hallelujah* / Schuman, *Prelude; Questions* / Schütz, *Anima mea; Heute ist Christus* / Slavenski / Verdi / Vierdanck.

B. DURATION 10–15 MINUTES. Bach, *Beruft* / Britten, *Ceremony; Missa brevis* / Carter / Couperin / Csonka / Dietrich, F. / Hand / Hasse / Lendvai, *Op. 5* / Loeffler / Lübeck / Thompson, *Rosemary* / Thomson, *Medea* / Vaughan Williams, *Magnificat; Willow-wood.*

C. DURATION 15 MINUTES OR MORE. Bacon, *From Emily's diary; Precepts* / Brahms, *Op. 17* / Busser / Caplet / Chabrier / Chandler / Debussy, *La demoiselle* / Dietrich, F. / von Dohnányi / Herrmann / Hindemith / Lamb / Lendvai, *Op. 20* / Pergolesi, *Stabat Mater* / Sanders / Vaughan Williams, *Riders; The shepherds* / Wagner.

D. WITH INSTRUMENTS (OTHER THAN KEYBOARD), OPTIONAL. Binchois (2 undesignated melody instruments) / Brahms, *Op. 17* (1 or 2 horns, harp) / Britten, *Ceremony* (harp) / Chandler (harp) / Cherubini (harp) / Ciconia (2 undesignated melody instruments) / Couperin (strings, Bc) /

169

Csonka (harp) / Dietrich, F. (2 flutes or recorders, 2 violins, cello or bassoon) / Grenon (2 undesignated melody instruments) / Hand (recorders) / Herrmann, *Op. 85* (harp) / Hinton (handbells or chime bars and recorders) / Holst, *Rig Veda* (violins); *Seven part songs* (strings) / Jones (lute) / Kindermann (2 violins, flute or oboe) / Kodály (piccolo) / Lang, *Op. 41* (3 violins, 1 viola) / Lantins (2 undesignated melody instruments) / Lassus, *Cantiones sine texte* (1 or 2 undesignated melody instruments) / Le Jeune (2 undesignated melody instruments) / Leoninus (1 undesignated melody instrument) / Lockwood (flute) / Loeffler (harp, 2 flutes, cello) / Lübeck (2 violins, flutes, oboes, or recorders) / Machault (1 undesignated melody instrument) / Mahler (glockenspiel, triangle) / Martinu, *The Ascension* (violin); *The birth of our Lord* (violin) / Marx, *Abendständchen* (recorder); *Drescherlied* (flute and percussion); *Halt hoch* (recorders, drum, violins I and II, viola, cello); *Ihr kleinen Vögelein* (flute, oboe, guitar, violin, cello); *Ihr müsst* (recorders, 2 flutes, xylophone, glockenspiel, percussion, 4 violins, viola, cello, bass) / Milhaud (harp, oboe, cello) / Nelson (harp) / Nicolaus Praepositus (2 undesignated melody instruments) / Ockeghem (2 undesignated melody instruments) / Pinkham (3 trombones, tuba) / Riegger (flute, 2 horns, bass) / Schuman, *Questions* (flute, strings) / Schütz, *Auf dem Gebirge* (2 gambas, 3 cellos); *Der Herr ist mein Licht* (2 undesignated melody instruments); *Was betrübst du dich* (2 undesignated melody instruments); *Wie ein Rubin* (2 undesignated melody instruments) / Smith, R. (horn, string trio) / Spitta (2 violins) / Thomson, *Medea* (percussion) / Vaughan Williams, *Magnificat* (flute and piano) / Vierdanck (2 undesignated melody instruments) / Warner (harp and strings) / Warrell (strings and wind instruments).

E. WITH ORCHESTRA, CHAMBER (SMALL, BRASS, ETC.). Bach, *Duets from the cantatas* (various instrumental combinations) / Bacon (small orchestra) / Cowell (2 trumpets, 2 trombones, organ, ad lib. timpani) / Diamond (String orchestra) / Gál, *Op. 5* (strings, clarinet, horn, harp or piano) / Hasse (string orchestra) / Hindemith (strings, winds, percussion) / Hovhannes (2 oboes, trumpets or clarinets, 2 horns or trombones, harp or piano) / Lendvai, *Op. 20* (small orchestra) / Marx, *Halt hoch* (recorders, drum, violins I and II, viola, cello); *Ihr müsst* (recorders, 2 flutes, xylophone, glockenspiel, percussion, 4 violins, viola, cello, bass) / Pergolesi (string orchestra) / Phillips (chamber orchestra) / Sanders (flute, string quartet, bass, 2 pianos) / Schuman, *Questions* (flute and strings) / Stravinsky, *Cantata* (2 flutes, oboe, English horn and cello) / Warrell (strings and winds).

F. WITH ORCHESTRA, FULL. Bartók, *Breadbaking; Don't leave me; Hussar; Lad's dance; Loafer; Lullaby; Only tell me; Teasing song; Wedding* / Berlioz / Brahms, *Op. 12* / Caplet, *Messe* / Chabrier / Debussy / Dohnányi / Fine, *Father William; The lobster quadrille; Lullaby of the duchess* / Freed / Holst, *Rig Veda* / Honegger / Lamb / Mendelssohn, *You spotted snakes; Through the house* / Mennin / Porpora / Roger-Ducasse / Schmitt / Schumann, arr by Pfitzner, *Frauenchöre* / Shepherd / Spelman / Vaughan Williams, *Land; Magnificat; Riders; Shepherds; Sigh; Willow-wood* / Wagner.

G. WITH SOLO(S), WOMEN. Bacon, *From Emily's diary* (SA) / Berlioz (SSA) / Beveridge (S) / Boulanger (S) / Britten, *Ceremony* (SS); *Missa brevis* (SSA) / Busser (S) / Caplet, *Inscriptions* (SSA); *Le miroir* (SSA) / Chabrier, *A la musique* (S); *La sulamite* (Mezzo S) / Clarke (S or T) / Copland (S) / Couperin (SS) / Cruft (S) / Debussy (Mezzo S) / Dietrich, F. (SA) / Dohnányi (SSA) / Fine, *Caroline* (SA); *White knight's song* (S) / Freed (Baritone or Mezzo S) / Gál, *Op. 5* (A) / Gédalge (A) / Greene (SA) / Hasse (SA) / Herrmann, *Op. 85* (S or T) / Honegger (SSA) / Lübeck (SA) / Mahler (A) / Mendelssohn, *Surrexit* (SSAA); *You spotted snakes* (SS) / Moore (S) / Pearson (S) / Pergolesi (SA) / Porpora, *Laetatus sum* (SA); *Magnificat* (S) / Riegger (SSAAA) / Rossini (S) / Salazar (SA) / San Juan (S) / Schubert, *Op. 134* (S); *Op. 135* (A) / Schuman, *Prelude* (S) / Spelman (S) / Spitta (S) / Stravinsky, *Cantata* (ST) / Thomson, *Medea* (SSA) / Vaughan Williams, *Magnificat* (A); *O taste* (S); *Riders* (SSA baritone); *Shepherds* (3 men soli, S); *Sigh no more* (A) / Voynich (SSA) / Walker (SSA).

H. WITH SOLO(S), MEN. Clarke (S or T) / Goodman (baritone) / Harris, A. (baritone) / Herrmann, *Op. 85* (S or T) / Stravinsky, *Cantata* (ST) / Thomas (baritone) / Vaughan Williams, *Riders* (SSA baritone); *Shepherds* (3 men soli, S); *Willow-wood* (baritone).

INDEX OF AUTHORS AND SOURCES OF TEXTS

A short title or first line may be given in parentheses after the author or source in those cases where a composer has many compositions listed. When an author or source is used more than once by a composer, a number in parentheses follows the composer's name. Author and source designations listed here are, in most cases, those given on the editions themselves, and therefore very incomplete.